Student Weekly Assessment

Macmillan/McGraw-Hill

The McGraw·Hill Companies

 Macmillan/McGraw-Hill

Published by Macmillan/McGraw-Hill, of McGraw-Hill Education, a division of The McGraw-Hill Companies, Inc.,
Two Penn Plaza, New York, New York 10121.

Printed in the United States of America

8 9 RHR 15

Contents

Sample Questions vii

Selection Tests

Book 1, Unit 1

Week 1 *Goin' Someplace Special* 3
Week 2 *Shiloh* 7
Week 3 *Maya Lin, Architect of Memory* 11
Week 4 *The Night of San Juan* 15
Week 5 *Sleds on Boston Common* 19

Book 1, Unit 2

Week 1 *Hidden Worlds* 23
Week 2 *Rattlers!* 27
Week 3 *These Robots Are Wild!* 31
Week 4 *Up in the Air: The Story of Balloon Flight* 35
Week 5 *Hurricanes* 39

Book 1, Unit 3

Week 1 *The Catch of the Day: A Trickster Play* 43
Week 2 *The Golden Mare, the Firebird, and the Magic Ring* 47
Week 3 *Tricky Tales* 51
Week 4 *Blancaflor* 55
Week 5 *The Unbreakable Code* 59

Contents

Book 2, Unit 4

Week 1 Spirit of Endurance 63

Week 2 Ultimate Field Trip 5 67

Week 3 Heroes in Time of Need 71

Week 4 Zathura 75

Week 5 Skunk Scout 79

Book 2, Unit 5

Week 1 Valley of the Moon 83

Week 2 Black Cowboy Wild Horses 87

Week 3 A Historic Journey 91

Week 4 Davy Crockett Saves the World 95

Week 5 When Esther Morris Headed West 99

Book 2, Unit 6

Week 1 Miss Alaineus 103

Week 2 Bravo, Tavo! 107

Week 3 A Dream Comes True 111

Week 4 Weslandia 115

Week 5 The Gri Gri Tree 119

© Macmillan/McGraw-Hill

Contents

Weekly Assessment

Book 1, Unit 1

Week 1 125
Week 2 133
Week 3 141
Week 4 149
Week 5 157

Book 1, Unit 2

Week 1 165
Week 2 173
Week 3 181
Week 4 189
Week 5 197

Book 1, Unit 3

Week 1 205
Week 2 213
Week 3 221
Week 4 229
Week 5 237

Contents

Book 2, Unit 4

Week 1 245
Week 2 253
Week 3 261
Week 4 269
Week 5 277

Book 2, Unit 5

Week 1 285
Week 2 293
Week 3 301
Week 4 309
Week 5 317

Book 2, Unit 6

Week 1 325
Week 2 333
Week 3 341
Week 4 349
Week 5 357

Read this selection. Then answer the questions that follow it.

Volcanoes

1   What creates volcanoes? Earth has volcanoes because its center, or core, is very hot. Volcanoes help cool the core. The core is filled with both solid and melted rock. Surrounding the core is the mantle and then the crust, the outer layer of Earth.

2   A volcano takes many years to form. Magma, or melted rock in the mantle, rises through cracks in the cooler rock above it. In time, the magma breaks through the crust. The spot where this takes place is the eruption hole. Magma that reaches Earth's surface becomes lava. Over time, lava builds up around the hole and forms a volcano.

3   Violent eruptions can be dangerous, yet they also bring valuable minerals and rich soil to the surface. Scientists study volcanoes and try to predict their behavior.

S-1 Volcanoes affect the core by —

  A heating up the core or center

  B bringing rich soil to the surface

  C lowering the core temperature

  D creating a mantle and crust

S-2 Before magma breaks the crust—

  F volcanoes form eruption holes

  G magma changes into hot lava

  H magma rises to the cooler rock

  J lava builds around the hole

DIRECTIONS

Read the introduction and the passage that follows. Then read each question and fill in the correct answer on your answer document.

Anthony wrote this story about his science project. He wants you to help him revise and edit his story. Read the story and think about some changes that Anthony should make. Then answer the questions that follow.

Ready for Lift Off!

(1) Ms. Jillian our science teacher, has assigned us an exciting new project. (2) First, we have to pick a partner to work with. (3) We must choose an interesting topic. (4) We have to choose it from a list by Monday. (5) I will be doing my project with my best friend, Jeremy. (6) We really want to work on a project about space shuttles. (7) We will research our topic at the public library! (8) We also plan on making a modul of a space shuttle out of clay and cardboard. (9) Together, Jeremy and I will make our project a success!

S-3 What change, if any, should be made to sentence 1?

  A Insert a comma before *our*

  B Remove comma after *teacher*

  C Change *science* to *sceince*

  D Make no change

S-4 What is the **BEST** way to combine sentences 3 and 4?

  F By Monday, we must choose a topic and a list.

  G We must choose a topic by Monday to put on a list.

  H By Monday, we must choose a topic from the list.

  J By Monday, we must choose a list from the topic.

Selection
Tests

Mc Graw Hill **Macmillan/McGraw-Hill**

Goin' Someplace Special

Use this selection to answer questions 1–10.

1 Look at the chart below and answer the question that follows.

Character	Setting
Asks for permission to go	Grandmother's house
Feels embarrassed	Southland Hotel
Feels sad and discouraged	
Answers a question confidently	Grand Music Palace

Which of these belongs in the empty box?

A On the school bus

B Blooming Mary's garden

C Monroe's Restaurant

D The public library

2 Mama Frances can best be described as —

F strong and independent

G angry and loud

H strict and demanding

J silly and funny

3 Why does 'Tricia Ann sit at the back of the bus?

A She likes the view from the back.

B There are no seats in the front.

C She wants to sit with Ms. Grannell.

D A law says she has to sit there.

4 When 'Tricia Ann leaves the Peace Fountain, she feels —

   F annoyed by Jimmy Lee's question

   G angered by Jim Crow signs

   H happy to see Blooming Mary

   J surprised there was no place to sit

5 What does 'Tricia Ann learn about Someplace Special from Blooming Mary?

   A 'Tricia Ann can get there herself if she remembers Mama Frances' words.

   B 'Tricia Ann and Blooming Mary should go there together.

   C 'Tricia Ann can get there if she walks through the Southland Hotel.

   D 'Tricia Ann should find a new place she considers special.

6 How does 'Tricia Ann change during this story?

   F She makes more friends.

   G She learns how to take a compliment.

   H She learns how to be more polite to people.

   J She becomes more confident.

7 Read this sentence from the story.

Crossing her fingers and closing her eyes, she <u>blurted</u> out her question.

The word <u>blurted</u> means —

   A whispered softly

   B asked carefully

   C said quickly

   D sang happily

8 Read this sentence from the story.

Don't you <u>know</u> nothing?

Which word is pronounced the same as the word <u>know</u>?

  F Now

  G No

  H Knew

  J New

9 Read this sentence from the story.

As the girl <u>approached</u>, a little boy spoke to her.

The word <u>approached</u> means —

  A came forward

  B understood

  C stepped aside

  D listened

GO ON ➡

10 What does the idea of going Someplace Special mean to 'Tricia Ann at the end
of the story? Explain your answer and support it with details from the story.

_____

_____

_____

_____

_____

_____

_____

BE SURE YOU HAVE RECORDED ALL OF YOUR ANSWERS
ON THE ANSWER DOCUMENT.

Shiloh

Use this selection to answer questions 1–10.

1 What is the most likely reason that Marty's parents do not mention the dog by name?

   A Shiloh has not learned his name yet.

   B It makes Marty upset to talk about Shiloh.

   C They do not want to get attached to Shiloh.

   D Shiloh is not the dog's real name.

2 Marty and his family are taking care of Shiloh because —

   F they like dogs

   G they need a hunting dog

   H the dog was wounded in a fight and needs care

   J Judd Travers asked them to take care of the dog

3 What makes Marty think his father likes the dog?

   A Dad fed and scratched Shiloh when he thought nobody was looking.

   B Dad asked Judd whether he could buy Shiloh.

   C Dad paid Doc Murphy's bill.

   D Dad gave the dog a name.

4 One day, Marty walks to Friendly because he —

   F is hungry

   G wants to buy something for Shiloh

   H needs to find a job

   J wants to take Shiloh for a walk

© Macmillan/McGraw-Hill

5 Why does Marty believe that Judd Travers has mistreated his dog?

  A Marty saw Judd hit Shiloh.

  B Judd says that he does not like dogs.

  C Shiloh cowers and shies away from Judd.

  D Judd sent a German shepherd to fight with Shiloh.

6 Why does Marty's friend David say that Shiloh is an old stray cat?

  F Marty does not want anyone to know that Shiloh is at his house.

  G David wants to convince his mother to get him a cat.

  H David's mother does not want him playing with a dog.

  J Marty wants David to be allowed to come back to his house.

7 Read this sentence.

Shiloh's going around the table, putting his nose in everyone's lap, looking <u>mournful</u>.

The word <u>mournful</u> means—

  A sad

  B scared

  C tired

  D unsure

8 Read this sentence from the story.

Nobody wants to hear his dog's been hurt, though, and we wanted to make sure he was going to pull through.

What does the phrase "pull through" mean?

F To push forward

G To survive

H To drag

J To become sick

9 Read this sentence.

Ma reaches down to pet him, making low sympathy noises in her throat.

The word sympathy means —

A surprised to see

B waking up

C looking very happy

D feeling sorry for

10 How does Judd Travers feel about Marty's family taking care of Shiloh?
Explain your answer and support it with details from the story.

_____

_____

_____

_____

_____

_____

_____

BE SURE YOU HAVE RECORDED ALL OF YOUR ANSWERS
ON THE ANSWER DOCUMENT.

Maya Lin, Architect of Memory

Use this selection to answer questions 1–10.

---

1 Which statement best describes Maya Lin?

A She enjoys crowds.

B She focuses on making art for children.

C She hopes to be praised for her work.

D She likes to solve problems.

2 What is the main idea of this article?

F Maya Lin uses mathematics to help her create art, designs, and memorials.

G Maya Lin is a gifted artist who uses quotes from Martin Luther King to help her create her work.

H Maya Lin appreciates learning and tries to read as many books on her subjects as she can.

J Maya Lin is a talented architect who takes the time to learn about her subjects in order to create her art.

3 Which detail from the article supports the idea that Maya Lin appreciates learning about history?

A *"You create your own message, and then it is out there on its own."*

B *She sent in the winning design for the Vietnam Veterans Memorial in Washington, D.C.*

C *Too young to remember the civil rights movement firsthand, Lin researched it for months while working on the design for the Civil Rights Memorial.*

D *"I'm trying to make people become involved with the piece on all levels," Lin said, "with the touch and sound of the water, with the words, with the memories."*

4 When veterans first saw the Vietnam Veterans Memorial, they were —

    F glad they were being recognized

    G angry with the monument's appearance

    H grateful for Maya Lin's hard work

    J surprised that so many people went to see it

5 Which of Maya Lin's projects includes a 12-foot granite disk covered by water?

    A The park at Charlotte Coliseum

    B Vietnam Veterans Memorial

    C The clock for a New York City train station

    D Civil Rights Memorial

6 At the Civil Rights Memorial, visitors can read a quotation from a speech by —

    F Maya Lin

    G Willie Edwards, Jr.

    H Martin Luther King, Jr.

    J Sarah Salter

7 Read this sentence from the article.

Lin's Vietnam Memorial does not present any artifacts of the Vietnam era.

What does the word artifacts mean?

    A Objects from a certain place and time

    B Marble statues

    C Carvings in wood

    D Paintings created with a special type of paint

8 Read this sentence from the article.

Too young to remember the civil rights movement firsthand, Lin researched it for months while working on the design for the Civil Rights Memorial.

Which word from this sentence suggests something that happened in the past?

F Firsthand

G Movement

H Researched

J Working

9 Read this sentence from the article.

Lin's message can be found in the memorial's <u>exhibits</u>.

Which word means about the same as <u>exhibits</u>?

A Visitors

B Artwork

C Displays

D Granite

GO ON ▶

10 How does mathematics help Maya Lin as an architect? Explain your answer and support it with details from the article.

_____

_____

_____

_____

_____

_____

BE SURE YOU HAVE RECORDED ALL OF YOUR ANSWERS
ON THE ANSWER DOCUMENT.

STOP

Selection Test

The Night of San Juan

> ## Use this selection to answer questions 1–10.

1 Look at the chart below and answer the question that follows.

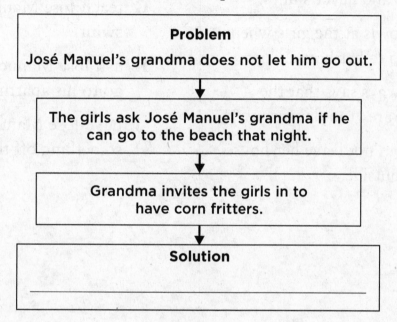

Problem

José Manuel's grandma does not let him go out.

↓

The girls ask José Manuel's grandma if he can go to the beach that night.

↓

Grandma invites the girls in to have corn fritters.

↓

Solution

_____

Which of these belongs on the blank line?

A Grandma asks the girls why they came to her house.

B Grandma tells the girls that José Manuel cannot go to the beach with them.

C Grandma calls the girls' mother and tells her José Manuel can join them at the beach.

D Grandma scowls at the girls and makes them feel embarrassed.

2 Why are the girls afraid of Grandma in the beginning of the story?

F She does not talk to many people and never smiles.

G She scowls at the girls when they go to her house.

H She always says that the streets are "too dangerous."

J She does not leave her house to go outside.

3 Why does José Manuel always play on the balcony?

A He likes the balcony because it is shaded from the sun.

B His grandma does not want him to play on the street.

C He enjoys watching the action on the street from above.

D His grandma does not like the neighborhood kids.

4 The girls put the note in the basket because they want to —

F have some of Grandma's corn fritters

G teach José Manuel how to swim

H ask José Manuel if they can go to his apartment

J have José Manuel drop something off the balcony

5 The girls invite José Manuel to the beach because they want to —

A celebrate the Night of San Juan

B play ball on the beach

C buy coconut sherbet

D teach José Manuel how to swim

© Macmillan/McGraw-Hill

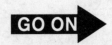

6 What lesson do the girls learn by the end of the story?

   F It is better to mind your own business.

   G You should not judge people before you know them.

   H Traditions are important to many people.

   J You should not go to someone's house unless you are invited.

7 Read this sentence from the story.

It was only my lonely friend José Manuel who was <u>forbidden</u> from joining us.

The word <u>forbidden</u> means —

   A ordered

   B requested

   C not allowed

   D not recommended

8 Read this sentence.

We chattered <u>excitedly</u> about our plans for that night.

What does <u>excitedly</u> mean?

   F Not excited

   G One who is excited

   H In an excited way

   J Excited again

9 Read this sentence from the story.

Even though Aitza was very <u>reluctant</u>, we convinced her to try our plan.

The word <u>reluctant</u> means —

   A disappointed

   B unwilling

   C confused

   D shy

10 What kind of person is Amalia? Explain your answer and support it with details from the story.

_____

_____

_____

_____

_____

_____

_____

BE SURE YOU HAVE RECORDED ALL OF YOUR ANSWERS
ON THE ANSWER DOCUMENT.

Sleds on Boston Common

Use this selection to answer questions 1–10.

1 Why were things difficult for people in Boston during December 1774?

   A The children could not go to school.

   B King George had come for a visit with the British soldiers.

   C The weather was stormy and cold.

   D Boston Harbor was closed and the people were losing money.

2 King George sent troops to Boston to —

   F make sure people in Boston followed the laws

   G help workers at Boston docks load ships

   H teach the people of Boston how to be soldiers

   J take over the Boston Common area

3 The children could not go sledding on Boston Common because —

   A they forgot their sleds

   B they had to attend school

   C the British soldiers had taken over the area

   D their fathers told them they could not go

4 Henry believes that Boston Common is owned by —

   F King George

   G children with sleds

   H the Sons of Liberty

   J all the people of Boston

5 Why do the soldiers glare at Henry when he speaks to General Gage?

A They don't want to move their tents and other equipment.

B They do not like children and want them to leave.

C They don't think it is respectful for a child to talk to the general.

D They do not want the boys to be able to have any fun.

6 Henry believes General Gage is a "good man" because the general —

F has children the same age as him

G takes the time to listen to him

H leaves Boston and takes the soldiers away

J lives in the biggest house in Boston

7 Read this sentence from the story.

King George wanted to punish those in Boston who spoke against his laws that were made across the sea: patriots like Sam Adams and John Hancock and other town leaders.

Which words in the sentence help the reader know what patriots means?

A *King George*

B *those in Boston*

C *spoke against his laws*

D *other town leaders*

GO ON

8 Read this sentence from the story.

One thing His Majesty King George couldn't stop was the winter snow in the <u>colony</u> of Massachusetts.

Which word is in the same word family as <u>colony</u>?

F Call

G Cold

H Colonize

J Column

9 Read this sentence from the story.

He leaned down to <u>inspect</u> the other sleds.

The word <u>inspect</u> means —

A look at

B build

C try out

D move

GO ON

10 What kind of person is Henry? Explain your answer and support it with details from the story.

_____

_____

_____

_____

_____

_____

BE SURE YOU HAVE RECORDED ALL OF YOUR ANSWERS
ON THE ANSWER DOCUMENT.

Hidden Worlds

Use this selection to answer questions 1–10.

1 Look at the chart below and answer the question that follows.

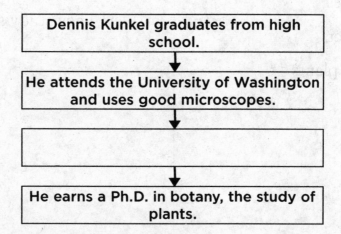

Dennis Kunkel graduates from high school.

He attends the University of Washington and uses good microscopes.

He earns a Ph.D. in botany, the study of plants.

Which of these belongs in the empty box?

A He goes to a junior college and works in the science lab.

B He goes to graduate school and studies tiny living things.

C He travels to the site of Mount St. Helens to do research.

D He works out of his home in Hawaii.

GO ON ▶

2 When he was ten, what did Dennis Kunkel look at under the microscope before he started collecting pond water?

F Pet fur

G Soil samples

H Dead objects

J Flowering plants

4 Why does the author say that scientists are explorers?

F They answer questions.

G They work in laboratories.

H They make discoveries.

J They study specimens.

3 What did Dennis Kunkel do during graduate school?

A He studied botany.

B He learned to use a microscope.

C He visited Mount St. Helens.

D He learned about the ocean.

5 What did Dennis Kunkel do after the eruption of Mount St. Helens?

A He tried to figure out why volcanoes erupt.

B He figured out why the ash from volcanoes is important.

C He discovered how long it takes for a volcano to become active again.

D He studied what happened to life in nearby lakes and streams.

6 What is one of the most important things you can do to become a scientist?

   F Watch, look, and listen to your surroundings

   G Take a tour of a laboratory

   H Talk to a scientist at a college

   J Buy a magnifying glass and a microscope

7 Read this sentence.

Dennis began to use the science department's electron microscopes for his own research.

What does the word research mean?

   A A careful study to find, collect, and learn facts

   B Examining microscopes

   C A book that contains scientific information

   D To look for something one more time

8 Read this sentence.

Dennis worked in labs with good microscopes and spent hours speaking with professors and students about science.

Which word in the sentence probably comes from a Greek root that means "to look"?

   F Science

   G Professors

   H Students

   J Microscopes

9 Read this sentence.

Helicopters hovered over the murky gray water.

The word murky means —

   A deep

   B cloudy

   C cold

   D shallow

10 Why is it important to explore the "hidden worlds," such as those that Dennis Kunkel explored? Explain your answer and support it with details from the article.

_____

_____

_____

_____

_____

_____

_____

BE SURE YOU HAVE RECORDED ALL OF YOUR ANSWERS
ON THE ANSWER DOCUMENT.

Rattlers!

Use this selection to answer questions 1–10.

---

1 How can the reader tell that this selection is a nonfiction article?

   A It includes illustrations of people.

   B It teaches a lesson with animal characters.

   C It gives important dates in history.

   D It gives facts about real living things.

2 What should a person do if he or she is bitten by a rattlesnake?

   F Remove the rattlesnake's fangs from the skin

   G Collect the rattlesnake's venom

   H Visit a doctor to receive treatment for the bite

   J Cover the wound with a bandage

3 Which statement about rattlesnakes is true?

   A Many older rattlesnakes have longer tails.

   B Rattlesnakes eat bison and other large animals.

   C Most rattlesnakes would rather hide than attack a person.

   D Rattlesnakes use their eyes to find prey.

4 Which statement explains why there are fewer rattlesnakes than there once were?

   F Humans have disturbed many places where rattlesnakes live.

   G Humans can survive if they are bitten by a rattlesnake.

   H Rattlesnakes are having fewer babies at one time.

   J The red-tailed hawk population is much larger today.

5 How are baby rattlesnakes born?

    A They swim out of the water.

    B They wriggle out of thin sacs.

    C They hatch from eggs.

    D They come out of the mother's pouch.

6 Hugh McCrystal's family catches rattlesnakes to —

    F try to get rid of the rattlesnakes in their area

    G study rattlesnakes in order to protect them

    H milk the venom from rare rattlesnakes

    J keep the rattlesnakes as pets

7 Read this sentence.

There are about 30 different species of rattlers, and you can find at least one kind or another in almost every state.

Which word in the sentence helps the reader understand the meaning of species?

    A State

    B Rattlers

    C Kind

    D Different

© Macmillan/McGraw-Hill

8 Read this sentence from the article.

When the snake <u>vibrates</u> its tail, the sections rattle against each other and make a buzzing sound.

What does <u>vibrates</u> mean?

F Hides

G Pumps venom

H Moves back and forth

J Makes noises

9 Read this sentence from the article.

How can <u>predators</u> eat a rattler without getting hurt?

The word <u>predators</u> means —

A young reptiles

B people who study snakes

C large snakes

D animals that hunt

10 How does a rattlesnake catch and eat a meal? Explain your answer and support it with details from the article.

_____

_____

_____

_____

_____

_____

_____

BE SURE YOU HAVE RECORDED ALL OF YOUR ANSWERS
ON THE ANSWER DOCUMENT.

These Robots Are Wild!

Use this selection to answer questions 1–10.

1 What was the author's purpose in writing this article?

   A To inform readers of new ideas in science

   B To convince readers that bugs are useful

   C To persuade readers to study science

   D To tell readers how to make a robot

2 The author uses subheadings in this article to —

   F provide a summary of the information in each section

   G make a list of topics that he or she will write about

   H explain what the pictures in the article show

   J give hints about information included in each section

3 Why is Roy Ritzmann interested in cockroaches?

   A He is making a robot that kills cockroaches and other insects.

   B He wants to make a robot that acts similarly to a cockroach.

   C He wants to protect cockroaches from people who think they are pests.

   D He is trying to learn how to use cockroaches in his everyday life.

4 Arthropods can respond quickly to changes in their environment because they have —

   F sensors on the outside of their bodies

   G very complicated brains

   H eyes on the back of their heads

   J quick-moving legs

5 Joseph Ayers made his robot like a lobster so it can use its —

   A legs to run very fast

   B hard shell to protect itself

   C sense of smell underwater

   D antennas to find prey

7 Read this sentence from the article.

Ritzmann has spent time investigating cockroaches.

What does the word investigating mean?

   A Examining

   B Improving

   C Finding

   D Creating

6 New robots sent to explore a planet such as Mars will be able to —

   F drill to the planet's center

   G travel easily over the planet's surface

   H carry humans safely to and from Earth

   J last forever without any source of power

GO ON

8 Read this sentence.

In developing and building new robots, scientists have observed cockroaches to see how their legs operate.

Which word from the sentence comes from a Latin root that means "watch"?

F Developing

G Building

H Observed

J Operate

9 Read this sentence from the article.

By behaving like humble bugs, the new generation of robots may help us gain some insight into the mysteries of the universe.

The word insight means —

A awareness

B comfort

C confidence

D satisfaction

© Macmillan/McGraw-Hill

10 How does the new generation of robots imitate nature? Explain your answer
and support it with details from the article.

_____

_____

_____

_____

_____

_____

Up in the Air: The Story of Balloon Flight

> ## Use this selection to answer questions 1–10.

1 Which sentence from the article gives an opinion?

  A *Today thousands of people in many parts of the world belong to balloon clubs.*

  B *Others, more daring, wanted to do what no one had done before.*

  C *Now there were two ways to send balloons aloft: with hot air and with hydrogen.*

  D *When the balloon was 200 feet in the air, the pair took off their hats and bowed to those below.*

2 What did brothers Joseph and Etienne Montgolfier do?

  F They witnessed the world's first public balloon flight.

  G They built and flew the world's first hot-air balloon.

  H They figured out that helium can make a balloon float.

  J They flew across the English Channel.

3 Professor Jacques A.C. Charles's lighter-than-air balloon was important because it —

  A was filled with hydrogen

  B held the first human passengers

  C was attacked by nervous villagers

  D proved that less oxygen exists high above Earth

4 Why were a duck, a rooster, and a lamb the first passengers to go up in a balloon?

   F Their weight was light enough for the basket to hold.

   G No one knew if people would be able to breathe far above Earth.

   H The air used to blow up the balloon was too hot for people to be near.

   J Everyone else was too frightened of being so far away from the ground.

5 Which statement is a fact about the first public balloon flight?

   A Eight men rode in the balloon.

   B The balloon sailed over Paris.

   C Many people thought it was amazing.

   D The balloon rose 6,000 feet into the air.

6 In the early 1900s, which flying object was made of several balloons?

   F A blimp

   G A cabin

   H A gondola

   J A plane

7 Read this sentence.

In 1783, two French brothers launched the world's first hot-air balloon.

What is the meaning of launched?

   A Put together

   B Set in motion

   C Filled with gas

   D Blew up

© Macmillan/McGraw-Hill

    Selection Test

8 Read this sentence.

Balloons have been lifted by smoke, hot air, helium, and hydrogen.

Which word from the sentence comes from a Greek root that means "water"?

F Lifted

G Smoke

H Helium

J Hydrogen

9 Read this sentence from the article.

He was <u>anchored</u> to the ground by a long rope called a tether.

The word <u>anchored</u> means —

A held

B pushed

C moved

D crowded

GO ON

10 Why do the balloons of today use helium instead of hydrogen? Explain your answer and support it with details from the article.

_____

_____

_____

_____

_____

_____

Hurricanes

Use this selection to answer questions 1–10.

1 Look at the web below and answer the question that
follows.

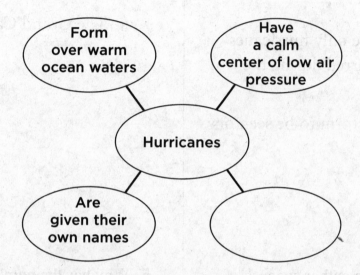

Which of these belongs in the empty oval?

A Have winds of at least 50 miles per hour

B Called cyclones and typhoons in other areas of the world

C Are more damaging than tornadoes

D Mainly occur during the winter along the East Coast

GO ON ➡

2 The author mentions Hurricane Andrew because it was —

F one of the worst storms ever to hit the United States

G the first storm to receive a name

H one of the only hurricanes that occurred during the 1990s

J the first storm to be seen on satellite

4 Where is the most dangerous place to be during a hurricane?

F A mountain range

G The Great Plains

H A coastal area

J The Grand Canyon

3 Why does the author suggest using a flashlight instead of a candle for emergency lighting during a hurricane?

A A flashlight gives off more light

B A candle may accidentally start a fire

C A flashlight is easier to find

D A candle may burn out too quickly

5 Why has the number of hurricane-related deaths in the United States decreased in recent years?

A There are fewer hurricanes than there used to be.

B Hurricanes today have lower wind speeds.

C More people evacuate the coastline than ever before.

D There are more advanced ways to warn people of a storm.

6 The author's purpose in writing this article was to —

F entertain readers with some shocking events

G persuade readers to evacuate their homes during a storm

H teach readers a lesson about life during hard times

J give readers important information about the weather

7 Read this sentence from the article.

Hurricanes are not really evil, but they can cause terrible destruction and great loss of life.

Which word means about the same as destruction?

A Death

B Damage

C Wave

D Winds

8 Read this sentence from the article.

Hurricane and storm warnings are broadcast over radio and television and are also available on the Internet.

The word available means that the warnings can be —

F used or found

G erased

H examined or studied

J changed

9 Read this sentence from the article.

Hurricane forecasts estimate when the eye will pass over a particular location.

Which definition of the word eye best fits the way it is used in this sentence?

A The hole on a needle

B To look for a hurricane

C The center of a storm

D An organ used to see with

GO ON

Student Name _____

10 How does technology help people prepare for hurricanes? Explain your answer and support it with details from the article.

_____

_____

_____

_____

_____

_____

_____

BE SURE YOU HAVE RECORDED ALL OF YOUR ANSWERS
ON THE ANSWER DOCUMENT.

Selection Test

The Catch of the Day: A Trickster Play

Use this selection to answer questions 1–10.

1 The fisher decides to trick the baker and the others because he wants to —

   A catch their fish

   B sell their items

   C take their money

   D get some food

2 Who tells the story to the children?

   F The basketmaker

   G The fisher

   H The Griot

   J The weaver

3 The fisher tells the people trying to use the bridge that —

   A their loads are too heavy to cross

   B he cannot catch any fish that day

   C they must swim across the river instead

   D the king's treasurer is charging a fee to cross

4 When the fisher first tells the basketmaker about the bridge, the basketmaker —

   F does not believe the fisher

   G runs to the village to spread the news

   H thanks the fisher for saving her

   J asks others for their opinion

5 The others realize they've been tricked when they —

   A talk to the king's treasurer

   B get to the village

   C return to the bridge

   D talk to the basketmaker

6 What does the fisher learn in the end?

   F He is not a good swimmer after all.

   G People who play tricks on others will be tricked themselves.

   H Most people do not find tricks very funny.

   J It is important to be honest if you want to make friends with others.

7 Which word best completes the analogy?

Unfortunate is to sad as <u>instruct</u> is to —

   A learn

   B listen

   C teach

   D wish

GO ON ▶

8 Read this sentence from the play.

Please, it is a token of my appreciation.

The word <u>appreciation</u> means —

F congratulations

G belongings

H thanks

J wealth

9 Read this sentence from the play.

It is the only way to get to the market to sell our <u>wares</u>.

What does the word <u>wares</u> mean?

A Goods

B Baskets

C Food

D Services

10 What is the setting of this story, and why is it important? Explain your answer
and support it with details from the play.

_____

_____

_____

_____

_____

_____

_____

| BE SURE YOU HAVE RECORDED ALL OF YOUR ANSWERS ON THE ANSWER DOCUMENT. | |

The Golden Mare, the Firebird, and the Magic Ring

> ## Use this selection to answer questions 1–10.

1 Look at the chart below and answer the question that follows.

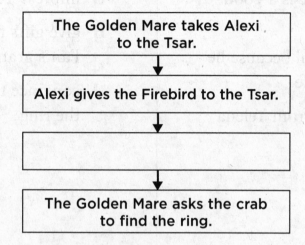

Which of these belongs in the empty box?

A Alexi finds a feather from the Firebird.

B Alexi brings Yelena the Fair to the Tsar.

C Alexi releases the Firebird from its cage.

D Alexi jumps into the Water of Youth.

GO ON ➡

2 Why does the Golden Mare help Alexi?

   F She is in love with him because he is kind.

   G She knows he is a good hunter.

   H She is grateful because he spared her life.

   J She is a gift from Yelena the Fair.

4 Alexi asks the Tsar for a tent and fine foods so that he can —

   F give the Golden Mare a good meal

   G impress Yelena the Fair

   H give gifts to Yelena the Fair's grandmother

   J convince the crab to find the ring

3 When the Tsar first meets Alexi, what does he want him to do?

   A Sell him the Golden Mare

   B Find the Firebird

   C Bring Yelena the Fair to him

   D Become his best huntsman

5 The Tsar asks Alexi to find Yelena the Fair's grandmother's ring because —

   A the Tsar wants to give it to her as a gift

   B the Tsar wants to sell the ring for a good price

   C Yelena the Fair's grandmother is ill

   D Yelena the Fair demands the ring so she can marry

6 What happens when the Tsar jumps into the cauldron?

F He is killed instantly.

G He turns into a baby.

H He swims to the bottom and finds the ring.

J He turns into a handsome young man.

8 Read this sentence from the story.

"Hold, fair sir, do not shoot," said the mare, to the astonishment of the lad.

Which word is pronounced the same as the word <u>fair</u>?

F Fear

G Fare

H Far

J Fir

7 Read this sentence.

Alexi left home to <u>seek</u> his fortune.

What does the word <u>seek</u> mean?

A Accept

B Search for

C Show

D Understand

9 Read this sentence.

Yelena <u>consented</u> to become his bride.

The word <u>consented</u> means —

A agreed

B prepared

C refused

D wanted

10 How does the Tsar treat Alexi? Explain why he treats him this way and support it with details from the story.

_____

_____

_____

_____

_____

_____

_____

BE SURE YOU HAVE RECORDED ALL OF YOUR ANSWERS
ON THE ANSWER DOCUMENT.

STOP

Tricky Tales

Use this selection to answer questions 1–10.
---

1 How are trickster tales different from written stories?

  A They are usually much longer.

  B They usually do not have happy endings.

  C They have animals for all the main characters.

  D They change over time.

2 How does Tchin get new material for his trickster stories?

  F He listens to stories children tell him.

  G He watches a lot of television.

  H He studies different ancient cultures.

  J He pays close attention to current events.

3 Trickster tales help to answer or explain questions about —

  A health and diet

  B natural events

  C leaders and politics

  D career choices

4 Tchin believes that stories, legends, and myths are really —

  F lessons

  G poems

  H true stories

  J fairy tales

5 Which character would most likely appear in a trickster tale?

  A Native American

  B Sneaky Snake

  C Siksika

  D Storyteller

6 What do almost all tricksters have in common?

  F They care for others.

  G They are sly.

  H They make friends easily.

  J They do bad things.

7 Read this sentence.

The history of trickster storytelling spans many generations.

What does the word generations mean?

  A Age groups

  B Cultures

  C Types of stories

  D Ideas

8 Read this sentence.

One tale reveals an amusing reason for why rabbits have long ears and short legs.

What does the word reveals mean?

F Confuses

G Explains

H Finds

J Uses

9 Read this sentence.

The Native American tradition of trickster storytelling has a rich history.

Which meaning of the word rich best fits the way it is used in this sentence?

A Having a lot of money

B Costly, elegant, or fine

C Strongly flavored

D Of great value or worth

10 What was the author's purpose in writing "Tricky Tales"? Explain your answer and support it with details from the article.

_____

_____

_____

_____

_____

_____

Blancaflor

Use this selection to answer questions 1–10.

1 What theme or lesson is expressed in this story?

A Never forget your friends.

B Look before you leap.

C Always keep your promises.

D Hard work brings rewards.

2 Why does the king get better?

F Prince Alfonso nurses him back to health.

G The doctors discover a new medicine for him.

H He is able to rest for a long time.

J A magical cure leads him to good health.

3 Prince Alfonso leaves home and sets off for the Land of No Return because —

A it is the only place he thinks he can find a bride

B he promised to do so in exchange for his father's cure

C he wants to live on his own away from his family

D he believes he will find a cure for his father's illness there

4 Prince Alfonso gives the eagle his chain so the eagle will —

F carry him across a ravine

G cure his father's illness

H introduce him to Blancaflor

J find the dragon ring

5 Prince Alfonso drops Blancaflor into the ocean because —

   A he is trying to get away

   B she tells him to

   C the eagle forces him to

   D he is afraid of her father

6 Blancaflor's father leaves Prince Alfonso safe at the end of the story because the prince has —

   F beaten him to the castle

   G been true to his word

   H given Blancaflor a good life

   J outsmarted him

7 Read this sentence.

Wizards had been <u>consulted</u>, and the queen had prepared herbal medicines.

The word <u>consulted</u> means —

   A offered a job

   B invited to dine

   C told the truth

   D asked for advice

GO ON

8 Read this sentence from the story.

His prolonged illness had left him with a renewed <u>urgency</u> for life.

What does <u>urgency</u> mean?

F Sense of peacefulness

G Wish for the future

H Need for immediate action

J Great understanding

9 Read this sentence from the story.

But if you do not complete the tasks, you will be food for my hounds.

The phrase "food for my hounds" means that the prince will —

A buy food for the dogs

B be killed by the dogs

C live with the dogs

D be turned into a dog

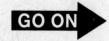

10 How does Blancaflor help Prince Alfonso complete the three tasks?
Explain your answer and support it with details from the story.

_____

_____

_____

_____

_____

_____

_____

The Unbreakable Code

Use this selection to answer questions 1–10.

1 Look at the chart below and answer the question that follows.

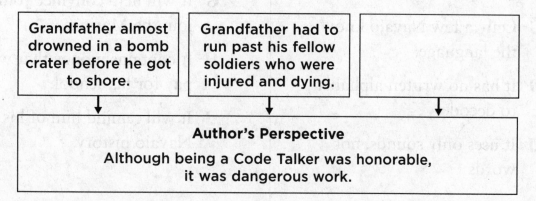

Grandfather almost drowned in a bomb crater before he got to shore.	Grandfather had to run past his fellow soldiers who were injured and dying.	

Author's Perspective

Although being a Code Talker was honorable, it was dangerous work.

Which clue belongs in the empty box?

A Grandfather's platoon had to memorize 200 military terms to code.

B Grandfather's platoon was tough and good at marching and hiking.

C Grandfather lay on the beach with gunfire flying past his ears.

D Grandfather could not tell anyone about the code when he got home.

---

2 When Grandfather was a young man at boarding school, he was forced to —

F break codes

G speak English

H join the Marines

J learn the Navajo language

3 According to Grandfather, how did he stay alive during the war?

A He held strong to his Navajo beliefs.

B He had a heavy radio pack.

C He used his good military training.

D He relied on his code-breaking skills.

GO ON ▶

4 What is the most likely reason the Navajo language is an "unbreakable code"?

F No one has heard it for hundreds of years.

G Only a few Navajo know the language.

H It has no written alphabet to decode.

J It uses only sounds, not words.

5 Why was Grandfather's platoon known as the toughest platoon at boot camp?

A They were good at following orders.

B They figured out the secret codes.

C They were used to difficult conditions.

D They knew how to get around in the desert.

6 Why does Grandfather give John his old wallet?

F It has pictures of Navajo soldiers.

G It will help convince John to join the Marines.

H It contains money that will pay for his school.

J It will remind him of his Navajo history.

7 Read this sentence.

The Japanese would trace our location to bomb us.

The word location means —

A position or place

B family history

C strength or force

D physical size

Selection Test

8 Read this sentence from the story.

They locked us in a classroom at the end of a long <u>corridor</u>.

What does the word <u>corridor</u> mean?

F Ran toward

G Tried to win

H Found out about

J Signed up

9 Read this sentence from the story.

Suddenly Grandfather's face looked as <u>creased</u> and battered as the canyon walls behind him.

What does the word <u>creased</u> mean?

A Painful

B Swollen

C Wrinkled

D Yellowed

10 Why did Grandfather want to join the Marines? Explain your answer and support it with details from the story.

_____

_____

_____

_____

_____

_____

_____

BE SURE YOU HAVE RECORDED ALL OF YOUR ANSWERS
ON THE ANSWER DOCUMENT.

Spirit of Endurance

Use this selection to answer questions 1–10.

---

1 Look at the chart below and answer the question that follows.

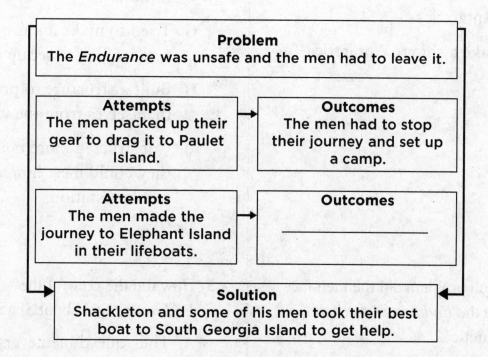

Which of these belongs on the blank line?

A The men had to stop their journey and build a camp on an ice floe.

B Shackleton hiked across the island to the whaling station.

C The men reached the island, but there was no one there to help them.

D The *Endurance* slipped through the ice and sank to the bottom of the ocean.

2 Shackleton wanted to be the first explorer to —

F explore the entire world

G reach Elephant Island

H travel all the way across Antarctica

J take a ship to Antarctica

3 Which problem did the men face once the *Endurance* reached Antarctica?

A Melting ice

B Bad weather

C Low amounts of food

D Poorly built life boats

4 What did the men on Elephant Island do while Shackleton and others left for South Georgia Island?

F Got more equipment off the *Endurance*

G Tried to make a journey to a new ice floe to set up camp

H Built a structure to protect themselves from the weather

J Constructed more boats so they could meet him at the whaling station

5 How did the crew of the *Endurance* feel about Shackleton?

A They questioned everything that Shackleton did.

B They thought Shackleton was a great storyteller.

C They were angry at Shackleton for putting them in danger.

D They trusted him and accepted his decisions.

GO ON ➤

Selection Test

6 How does the reader know that this article is nonfiction?

    F It tells an exciting adventure story.

    G It tells a made-up story about interesting characters.

    H It takes place in a faraway land.

    J It gives facts and details about real people and events.

7 Read this sentence from the article.

What if they were forced to abandon the ship?

The word abandon means —

    A clean up

    B take apart

    C leave behind

    D make stronger

8 Read this sentence.

Elephant Island was solid ground, but it was also uninhabited.

The word uninhabited means that —

    F the weather was terrible

    G it was covered with ice

    H no one lived there

    J the men had bad habits

9 Read this sentence from the article.

After two hours of backbreaking labor, they were only a mile from *Endurance*.

Which word means the same as labor?

    A Decisions

    B Hiking

    C Weather

    D Work

10 Why is "Spirit of Endurance" a good title for this article? Explain your answer and support it with details from the article.

_____

_____

_____

_____

_____

_____

_____

BE SURE YOU HAVE RECORDED ALL OF YOUR ANSWERS
ON THE ANSWER DOCUMENT.

Selection Test

Ultimate Field Trip 5

Use this selection to answer questions 1–10.

---

1 Look at the chart below and answer the question that follows.

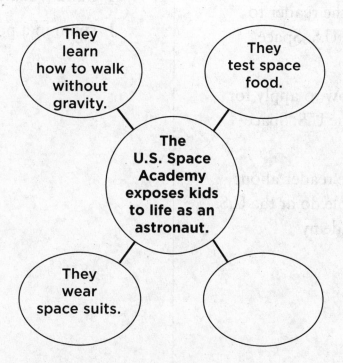

Which of these belongs in the empty oval?

A They experience how it feels to blast off.

B They launch a rocket to the moon.

C They learn how to play hockey without gravity.

D They build a special kind of chair.

2 The author's purpose in writing this article was to —

   F tell the reader an exciting story about the U.S. Space Academy

   G persuade the reader to attend the U.S. Space Academy

   H explain how to apply for camp at the U.S. Space Academy

   J inform the reader about what people do at the U.S. Space Academy

3 A good way to get around on the moon is to —

   A leap high

   B walk quickly

   C bunny hop

   D crawl on all fours

4 An astronaut on a space walk may have to —

   F eat dinner

   G make a repair

   H build a chair

   J swim in a pool

5 The kids at the Space Academy used the 5DF Chair to —

   A get used to weightless movement in space

   B gain control of a tumbling spacecraft

   C learn how to eat on the moon

   D practice working as a team

6 How do the simulator machines help students learn about space travel?

   F They show astronauts using space equipment.

   G They let students feel what being in space is like.

   H They let astronauts talk about their experiences.

   J They allow students to tour a real spacecraft.

8 Read this sentence.

   John waited while Paul adjusted the chair.

   The word adjusted means —

   F removed from the room

   G changed to fit a need

   H learned to use a tool

   J broke into smaller pieces

7 Read this sentence from the article.

   Then, Europa blasted off on a mission of its own.

   The word mission means a —

   A training session

   B special assignment

   C new idea

   D walk on the moon

9 Read this sentence from the article.

   "Europa, the training center is a dirt-free zone," said Paul.

   What does the word zone mean?

   A A gym where you can work out

   B An imitation spaceship

   C An area used for a certain activity

   D A set of equipment

© Macmillan/McGraw-Hill

10 How do students at the Space Academy learn about teamwork? Explain your answer and support it with details from the article.

_____

_____

_____

_____

_____

_____

_____

BE SURE YOU HAVE RECORDED ALL OF YOUR ANSWERS
ON THE ANSWER DOCUMENT.

STOP

Selection Test

Heroes in Time of Need

Use this selection to answer questions 1–10.

1 In this article, what is the author's message about natural disasters?

  A They can bring out the best in people.

  B They cause damage that cannot be repaired.

  C They occur more often than they should.

  D They make people feel helpless and scared.

2 In Santa Barbara, Avery Hardy set up a lemonade stand to raise money for victims of —

  F a war in India

  G the tsunami in South Asia

  H Hurricane Katrina

  J the earthquake in Asia

3 Which statement from the article is an opinion?

  A *The quake destroyed entire villages and killed about 80,000 people.*

  B *Acting like heroes, people donated time and money to help survivors of these natural disasters.*

  C *Plenty of kids joined grown-ups to hold fund-raisers in their communities and schools.*

  D *Countries all over the world sent equipment, food, blankets, doctors, tents, medicines, and other resources to help victims recover.*

GO ON ➡

4 The author mentions former presidents Bill Clinton and George H.W. Bush in this article to —

F show that two opponents came together to help victims of tragedy

G prove that the United States helped with the cleanup efforts

H explain that world leaders gave a lot of money to help with the tragedy

J describe how the president of the United States responded to a disaster

5 Project Backpack provided the youngest survivors of Hurricane Katrina with backpacks full of —

A baked goods

B school supplies

C money

D clothing

6 Which area experienced a tsunami in 2004?

F The Gulf Coast of the United States

G Coastlines from Southern India to Indonesia

H Parts of Afghanistan and India

J Villages in Pakistan

7 Read this sentence from the article.

Those who survived this disaster had no shelter.

What does the word survived mean?

A Lived through

B Received aid from

C Heard about

D Watched closely

GO ON

Selection Test

© Macmillan/McGraw-Hill

8 Read this sentence.

People <u>donated</u> time and money to help survivors.

The word <u>donated</u> comes from a Latin root that means —

F home

G time

H love

J give

9 Read this sentence.

Layo Obamehinti is one example of a kid who got <u>involved</u> in the rescue efforts.

In this sentence, the word <u>involved</u> means —

A caught up

B discovered

C helped

D slowed down

GO ON

10 In addition to loss of life, what other tragedies result from natural disasters? Explain your answer and support it with details from the article.

_____

_____

_____

_____

_____

_____

_____

BE SURE YOU HAVE RECORDED ALL OF YOUR ANSWERS
ON THE ANSWER DOCUMENT.

Zathura

Use this selection to answer questions 1–10.

1 Why is Walter pulling Danny's nose in the beginning of the story?

   A Danny wants him to play a game.

   B Danny keeps asking him to play baseball.

   C Danny broke his walkie-talkie.

   D Danny pulled his ears first.

2 What does Danny find under the tree?

   F His baseball

   G A robot

   H Pictures of outer space

   J A box

3 What happens when Danny first starts playing with the Zathura game pieces?

   A He floats to the ceiling.

   B Walter ties him to the couch.

   C A robot appears.

   D Meteors crash through the ceiling.

4 What happens after Walter throws the dice for the last time?

   F He floats toward the hole in the ceiling.

   G He is swallowed by a black hole.

   H He meets the Zorgon pirate.

   J He is chased by a robot.

5 What does Walter do with the game at the end of the story?

A Throws it away

B Gives it to his brother

C Leaves it by the tree

D Gives it to his parents

6 What does Danny mean when he says, "Looks like we keep on playing or we're up here forever"?

F He wants to fix the hole in the roof.

G He thinks the only way back to Earth is to finish the game.

H He wants to keep playing because he is bored.

J He thinks his parents will not come home until they finish the game.

7 Read this sentence from the story.

"Your robot is <u>defective</u>," Walter read.

What does <u>defective</u> mean?

A Has a weakness or problem

B Has been fixed

C Is very large and strong

D Is coming closer

© Macmillan/McGraw-Hill

8 Which word best completes the analogy?

Meteor is to space rock as <u>token</u> is to –

  F game piece

  G card trick

  H game board

  J baseball glove

9 Read this sentence from the story.

He <u>staggered</u> forward as the pirate's scaly tail and lizardlike legs swung down from the hole.

The word <u>staggered</u> means —

  A stood upright

  B walked unsteadily

  C moved around

  D fell down

GO ON ➡

10 How does Danny and Walter's relationship change as they play the game? Explain your answer and support it with details from the story.

_____

_____

_____

_____

_____

_____

BE SURE YOU HAVE RECORDED ALL OF YOUR ANSWERS
ON THE ANSWER DOCUMENT.

Skunk Scout

Use this selection to answer questions 1–10.
---

1 Why is Teddy upset by Uncle Curtis's driving?

  A He wants to get to the campsite quickly.

  B He wants to be the navigator.

  C Uncle Curtis keeps missing the freeway exit.

  D Uncle Curtis does not use maps to find his way.

2 What is the first thing Uncle Curtis and the boys do when they arrive at the campsite?

  F Put on bug spray

  G Set up the tent

  H Find wood for the campfire

  J Cook the hot dogs

3 Teddy offers to hammer the tent's stakes into the ground because he wants to —

  A get some exercise

  B build up the muscles in his arms

  C show Uncle Curtis who is boss

  D prove he is better than his brother

4 Teddy gets angry at the raccoon because it —

  F scares him when he comes out of the tent

  G makes a mess inside the tent

  H is not scared of him

  J eats almost all the marshmallows

© Macmillan/McGraw-Hill

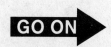

5 What is the main setting of this story?

A The freeway

B San Francisco

C Uncle Curtis's backyard

D A campsite at Mount Tamalpais

6 How does Teddy feel toward Bobby?

F He likes to compete with Bobby.

G He does not like how babyish Bobby seems.

H He does not like to play with Bobby.

J He thinks that Bobby is really a show-off.

7 Read this sentence from the story.

It's guaranteed to make you feel so tired, you won't notice any rocks.

What does the word guaranteed mean?

A Thought

B Believed

C Promised

D Pretended

GO ON

8 Read this sentence.

Uncle Curtis made the mistake of staying close to <u>supervise</u>.

The word <u>supervise</u> means —

F do a difficult job

G laugh at someone

H watch and direct

J write instructions for

9 Read this sentence from the story.

By the time this had happened to three more hot dogs, I tried to use a stick to <u>ease</u> them out of the coals.

Which definition of the word <u>ease</u> best fits the way it is used in this sentence?

A Freedom from pain or worry

B To lighten or lessen

C A relaxed manner without stiffness

D To move slowly or carefully

10 What kind of person is Uncle Curtis? Explain your answer and support it with details from the story.

_____

_____

_____

_____

_____

_____

_____

Valley of the Moon

> **Use this selection to answer questions 1–10.**

1 Look at this diagram of information from the story.

Cause	→	Effect
Miguela gets angry when Señor Johnston brings her a diary.	→	Miguela throws the diary off the balcony.
Rosalia has no place to hide the diary.	→	
Miguela sees Rosalia with the diary and makes a mean comment.	→	Rosalia feels hurt.

Which idea belongs in the empty space on the chart?

A Rosalia keeps the diary under her bed in the servants' quarters.

B Rosalia writes during siesta while everyone else is asleep.

C Rosalia keeps the diary tied to her waist and hidden under her skirt.

D Rosalia uses beet juice and a feather to write in the diary.

2 How does Rosalia first come to own the diary?

F Miguela gives it to her.

G She takes it out of the fountain.

H Señor Johnston gives it to her.

J She finds it hidden in the bushes.

3 Most of the new people arriving in Alta California were —

A farmers from Missouri

B trappers from Oregon

C sailors from Mexico

D padres from Spain

4 Why does Rosalia keep it a secret that she knows how to read and write?

F She does not want to show off her cleverness.

G She is a servant and should be working.

H She does not want her brother to be jealous.

J She wants to surprise the Medina family.

5 Rosalia never writes while in her room at night because —

A there is not enough light to see

B she doesn't want Miguela to catch her

C Ramona may wake up and see her

D she is too tired from working all day

6 How does Señor Johnston help Rosalia at the end of the story?

  F He gives her another diary.

  G He helps her learn how to write better.

  H He gives her real ink and quills.

  J He hides the diary in a safe place for her.

8 Read this sentence.

One finely embroidered hanging depicts the Holy Virgin.

Which word from a thesaurus means the same as depicts?

  F Honors

  G Treasures

  H Understands

  J Shows

7 Read this sentence from the story.

It was obvious that our father had been a white man.

The word obvious means —

  A very clear

  B unfortunate

  C good luck

  D well developed

9 Read this sentence from the story.

Ramona saves scraps of cloth from the sewing projects.

Which word means the same as projects?

  A Plans

  B Bulges

  C Activities

  D Curves

10 What kind of person is María Rosalia? Explain your answer and support it with details from the story.

_____

_____

_____

_____

_____

_____

_____

BE SURE YOU HAVE RECORDED ALL OF YOUR ANSWERS
ON THE ANSWER DOCUMENT.

    Selection Test

Black Cowboy Wild Horses

Use this selection to answer questions 1–10.

1 Why does Bob Lemmons leave the corral at the beginning of the story?

A To teach Warrior how to camp outside

B To smell the sun, moon, and stars

C To find a herd of mustangs

D To take Warrior to another ranch

2 Bob does not make a fire on the first night of his ride because he —

F does not want Warrior to be frightened

G knows it will be too hard to light because of the rain

H does not want the other horses to smell the smoke

J is too tired to collect wood for the fire

3 Throughout the story, it seems that Warrior would like to —

A ride free with the mustangs forever

B find more food to eat

C hide from the thunder and lightning

D be the father of a colt

4 Why does the stallion not have the heart to fight near the end of the story?

F He is feeling dizzy from the snake bite.

G He is confused by what is happening.

H He knows Warrior should be the leader.

J He is sad about the death of the colt.

5 How did Bob learn so much about animals in the wild?

   A He read books about them.

   B He listened to cowboys.

   C He watched his father raise horses.

   D He studied their movement and behavior.

6 Bob can best be described as —

   F patient

   G uncertain

   H nervous

   J excited

7 Read this sentence.

The horse reared, eager to gallop across the <u>vastness</u> of the plains.

The word <u>vastness</u> means —

   A dusty trails

   B enormous size

   C bright light

   D deep silence

GO ON

8 Read this sentence from the story.

Bob heard the faint but <u>distinct</u> rumbling of thunder.

The word <u>distinct</u> means —

F loud

G clear

H frightening

J demanding

9 Which word best completes the analogy?

Triumphant is to unsuccessful as <u>enthusiasm</u> is to —

A weariness

B movement

C nervousness

D excitement

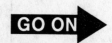

10 What was the author's purpose in writing this story? Explain your answer and support it with details from the story.

_____

_____

_____

_____

_____

_____

STOP

Selection Test

A Historic Journey

> **Use this selection to answer questions 1–10.**

1 What was the Louisiana Purchase?

  A Land sold to the United States from France

  B A journey across the United States

  C The name of an important trade

  D A river that reached the Pacific Ocean

2 President Jefferson asked Lewis and Clark to —

  F capture Native Americans

  G build towns and villages

  H explore the new territory

  J construct roads and bridges

3 Which animal were Lewis and Clark fascinated by in the beginning of their journey?

  A A prairie dog

  B A city rat

  C A horse

  D A mule deer

4 According to the article, "feasts of fresh buffalo were just pleasant memories" in the winter of 1804 –1805 because —

  F the men decided to eat other animals instead

  G the men ran out of arrows to catch the buffalo

  H Native Americans prevented the men from hunting

  J all of the buffalo had left the area

© Macmillan/McGraw-Hill

5 What was one thing Thomas Jefferson wanted Lewis and Clark to do, but they did not accomplish?

   A Find a water route to the Pacific Ocean

   B Capture animals and plants

   C Keep journals about their adventures

   D Draw maps and diagrams

6 The author thinks Lewis and Clark were good explorers because they —

   F covered a lot of ground very quickly

   G took detailed notes of everything they saw

   H tried their best to spell words correctly

   J gave nicknames to animals they observed

7 Read this sentence.

Each of these two army captains was an excellent <u>naturalist</u>.

What does the word <u>naturalist</u> mean?

   A A person who studies nature

   B Without nature

   C The state of being part of nature

   D Filled with nature

GO ON

Selection Test

8 Read this sentence from the article.

They crossed the Badlands—a harsh, nearly <u>vacant</u> area of rolling hills and little vegetation—and moved onto the plains.

Which word means the opposite of <u>vacant</u>?

F Mean

G Full

H Scary

J Beautiful

9 Read this sentence.

They produced descriptions of the <u>diverse</u> plant and animal life in the territory.

The word <u>diverse</u> means —

A difficult to understand

B of different kinds

C smooth to the touch

D easy to identify

10 What was the most important result of Lewis and Clark's expedition? Explain your answer and support it with details from the article.

_____

_____

_____

_____

_____

_____

_____

BE SURE YOU HAVE RECORDED ALL OF YOUR ANSWERS
ON THE ANSWER DOCUMENT.

Davy Crockett Saves the World

Use this selectiom to answer questions 1–10.

1 Why is the world in trouble when the story begins?

   A The president has a huge pile of letters.

   B The president cannot find Davy Crockett.

   C A comet is about to crash into the planet.

   D Davy does not know anything about comets.

2 Why is Davy going to visit Sally Sugartree?

   F To dance with her

   G To ask her to marry him

   H To read her newspaper

   J To show her his pet bear

3 What does Sally Sugartree show Davy?

   A A fifty-foot hickory tree

   B An illustration of a comet

   C A map of Washington

   D An ad in the newspaper

4 Davy's decision to go see the president is an important event in the plot because Davy will —

   F get to read a newspaper

   G help the president stop the comet

   H find the tallest mountain

   J be able to climb Eagle Eye Peak

GO ON ➡

5 Halley's Comet tries to get Davy off its back by —

A jumping into the Mississippi River

B spinning him around seventeen times

C diving into the Atlantic Ocean

D climbing to the top of Eagle Eye Peak

6 Why is Davy able to overcome Halley's Comet?

F The ocean puts out its fire.

G Death Hug grabs its tail.

H The sun doesn't shine as bright.

J It gets caught in a thunderstorm.

7 Read this sentence.

Davy <u>sauntered</u> off toward Sally Sugartree's cabin just as easy as you please.

What does <u>sauntered</u> mean?

A Walked slowly

B Hopped up and down

C Jumped around

D Ran with purpose

GO ON

Selection Test

8 Read this sentence.

Even though it was night,
the entire <u>countryside</u> lit up.

What does the word <u>countryside</u>
mean?

F The leader of a country

G A person who lives on
a farm

H A large area of land

J The border between
two places

9 Read this sentence.

Then he <u>commenced</u> to climb
all the way to the top of Eagle
Eye Peak.

Which word means the same as
<u>commenced</u>?

A Agreed

B Learned

C Started

D Wanted

© Macmillan/McGraw-Hill

10 What kind of person is Davy Crockett? Explain your answer and support it
with details from the story.

_____

_____

_____

_____

_____

_____

_____

BE SURE YOU HAVE RECORDED ALL OF YOUR ANSWERS
ON THE ANSWER DOCUMENT.

Selection Test

When Esther Morris Headed West

> ## Use this selection to answer questions 1–10.

1 Look at the diagram of information from the article.

Fact	Opinion
Colonial William Bright proposed that the women of Wyoming Territory be allowed to vote and hold office.	

Which idea belongs in the empty box?

A Esther Morris decided to apply for the position of Justice of the Peace.

B The proposed law was voted on in 1869.

C Newspapers ran many articles about the decision.

D The men who voted in favor of the law were reckless copperheads.

---

2 Esther Morris expressed the opinion that women should be able to —

  F go to school

  G look for gold

  H hold public office

  J earn their own money

3 The Wyoming legislature's job was to —

  A make or change laws

  B run banks

  C build roads and bridges

  D organize meetings

© Macmillan/McGraw-Hill

GO ON ➡

4 What did Esther Morris do when Ben Sheeks apologized for his behavior in the courtroom?

F She said he had good reason to act the way he did.

G She asked him to leave the courtroom.

H She asked him to give her the old court docket.

J She told him to apologize to the other lawyer.

6 According to the author, Wyoming was a good place for Esther Morris because she —

F had some wide-open ideas

G wanted to find gold

H needed to find a new job

J had many friends who lived there

5 In 1920, a professor from the University of Wyoming gathered stones in South Pass City to —

A keep as souvenirs

B build a new house

C make a memorial

D give them to the residents

7 Read this sentence.

I feel that my work has been satisfactory.

The word satisfactory means —

A in progress

B good enough

C outstanding

D very difficult

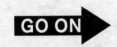

Selection Test

8 Read this sentence from the article.

Somewhere along the way he took up the crazy <u>notion</u> that women should be able to vote and hold office the same as men.

Which word means the same as <u>notion</u>?

F Misunderstanding

G Speech

H Examination

J Idea

9 Read this sentence.

Her personal <u>physician</u> determined that voting had no ill effects on a woman's health.

The word <u>physician</u> comes from a root word that means —

A natural science

B government

C education

D court judge

10 What was the author's purpose in writing "When Esther Morris Headed West"? Explain your answer and support it with details from the article.

_____

_____

_____

_____

_____

_____

BE SURE YOU HAVE RECORDED ALL OF YOUR ANSWERS
ON THE ANSWER DOCUMENT.

Selection Test

Miss Alaineus

Use this selection to answer questions 1–10.

---

1 Look at the web below and answer the question that follows.

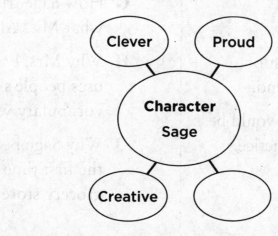

Which of the following belongs in the empty oval?

A Lonely

B Serious

C Bored

D Scared

GO ON

2 Why did Sage stay home on Vocabulary Day?

　F She caught a cold from a boy in class.

　G She already had her vocabulary words.

　H She could get the list of words from her friend.

　J She was afraid she would be late for baseball practice.

3 Why does Sage make up her own definitions for the vocabulary words?

　A She wants to entertain her classmates.

　B She is too lazy to look for the definitions.

　C She has trouble using the dictionary.

　D Her friend Starr already looked them up.

4 What does the author explain to the reader in the flashback?

　F Why Sage never uses a dictionary

　G How Sage tries to figure out what Miss Alaineus means

　H Why Mrs. Page rarely uses people's names for vocabulary words

　J Why Sage became confused the first time she went to the grocery store

5 Why is Sage embarrassed during the Vocabulary Bee?

　A She has left her homework at home.

　B She misspells all the vocabulary words.

　C She has to go to the back of the line after her turn.

　D She misspells her word and gives the wrong definition.

© Macmillan/McGraw-Hill

 **GO ON**

Selection Test

Student Name _____

6 For the Vocabulary Parade, Sage dresses as —

F Miss Stake, Queen of All People Who Make Mistakes

G Miss Alaineus, Queen of All Miscellaneous Things

H Precipitation, with a "watering-can hat"

J the word *capable*, with a cape

7 At the end of the story, Sage feels —

A surprised that her friends teased her

B proud of the costume she and her mother made

C confused because people did not like her costume

D sad because she no longer has a chance to go to the museum

8 Read this sentence.

Starr is not a luminous celestial object seen as a point of light in the sky.

What does the word luminous mean?

F Very hot

G Very red

H Very bright

J Very large

9 Read this sentence.

Mr. Bell smiled at his soggy clothes.

The word soggy means the same as —

A colorful

B huge

C dirty

D wet

GO ON

10 Why is Sage's definition of Miss Alaineus during the Vocabulary Bee an important event in the plot? Explain your answer and support it with details from the story.

_____

_____

_____

_____

_____

_____

BE SURE YOU HAVE RECORDED ALL OF YOUR ANSWERS
ON THE ANSWER DOCUMENT.

Bravo, Tavo!

> **Use this selection to answer questions 1–10.**

1 Look at the diagram of information about the story.

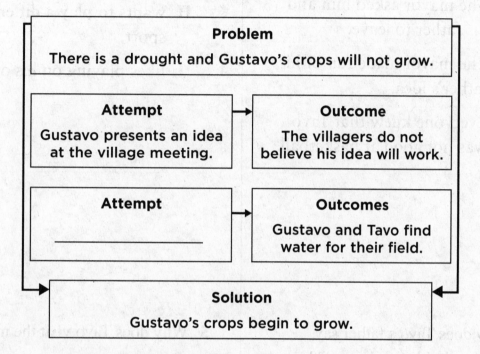

Problem
There is a drought and Gustavo's crops will not grow.

Attempt
Gustavo presents an idea at the village meeting.

→ **Outcome**
The villagers do not believe his idea will work.

Attempt
_____

→ **Outcomes**
Gustavo and Tavo find water for their field.

Solution
Gustavo's crops begin to grow.

Which idea belongs on the blank line?

A Gustavo marches to the front of the room and faces the crowd.

B Gustavo tells Tavo that he cannot buy new sneakers.

C Gustavo asks Señora Rosa to share her water.

D Gustavo and Tavo dig a *zanja* to the mountain.

2 Why was Tavo embarrassed when he left the village meeting?

  F Everyone saw Tavo's tattered old sneakers.

  G The mayor asked him and his father to leave.

  H The mayor made fun of his father's idea.

  J Everyone knew that Tavo was not good at basketball.

3 Why does Tavo's father say, "Even witches need water"?

  A Señora Rosa's garden is dying.

  B Señora Rosa fixes Tavo's sneakers.

  C Señora Rosa cannot get her own water.

  D He wants Señora Rosa to help dig the zanja.

4 Tavo stops practicing basketball with his team because he —

  F has to plant corn

  G loses his sneakers

  H wants to play a different sport

  J likes playing on his own

5 Why does Tavo visit the mayor?

  A To show the mayor that his father's idea worked

  B To invite the mayor to come to the basketball game

  C To ask for the mayor's help with digging the *zanja*

  D To give the mayor a cornstalk

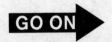

Selection Test

6 What does Tavo change his mind about at the end of the story?

   F Getting a new pair of sneakers

   G Thinking Señora Rosa is a witch

   H Wanting to play basketball

   J Spending time with his father

7 Read this sentence.

Tavo looked down as he kicked at the parched earth.

The word parched means —

   A brown

   B hard

   C dry

   D dirty

8 Read this sentence.

Tavo used duct tape to hold together his frayed sneakers.

What does the word frayed mean?

   F Very worn

   G Very old

   H Very useful

   J Very stained

9 Read this sentence from the story.

Jubilant, they danced in its wake.

What does the word jubilant mean?

   A Attentive

   B Surprised

   C Confident

   D Happy

 GO ON

10 How does Tavo solve the problem of needing new sneakers? Explain your answer and support it with details from the story.

_____

_____

_____

_____

_____

_____

_____

BE SURE YOU HAVE RECORDED ALL OF YOUR ANSWERS
ON THE ANSWER DOCUMENT.

STOP

A Dream Comes True

> ## Use this selection to answer questions 1–10.

1 How are Boundless Playgrounds different from most playgrounds in the United States?

  A They have lots of swings.

  B They do not cost much to build.

  C Millions of children use them.

  D They have equipment for children with disabilities.

2 On a playground, chime walls are used to —

  F prove to parents that playgrounds are not dangerous

  G convince people that more playgrounds should be built

  H encourage children with disabilities to use a swing

  J help children with vision problems enjoy sound

3 Why did Amy Jaffe Barzach design the playground called Jonathan's Dream?

  A She thought her town needed a new playground.

  B She wanted to honor her son who had disabilities.

  C She was very good at designing special equipment.

  D She had a lot of money and wanted to put it to good use.

4 What was impressive about Matthew Cavedon's swing glider invention?

  F He was very young when he came up with the idea.

  G He drew a very complicated design.

  H He built the swing with his own hands.

  J He helped raise money to buy the materials for the swing.

5 Matthew Cavedon hopes that Boundless Playgrounds will help —

  A him earn money someday

  B others interact with people who have different abilities

  C him prepare for an Olympic wheelchair team

  D convince parents that children with disabilities should move to Connecticut

6 What was the author's purpose in writing this article?

  F To inform readers about playgrounds in Connecticut

  G To persuade readers that all children deserve to play on playgrounds

  H To convince readers to build their own Boundless Playgrounds

  J To teach readers how to use the equipment in a Boundless Playground

7 Read this sentence from the article.

The <u>elementary</u> idea behind Boundless Playgrounds is that play is both part of the joy of childhood and an important way for children to learn about the world.

The word <u>elementary</u> means —

  A school

  B children

  C simple

  D helpful

8 Read this sentence.

Some people have <u>rigid</u> ideas about the way a playground should be built.

What does the word <u>rigid</u> mean?

F Energetic

G Original

H Strict

J Uncertain

9 Read this sentence.

Kids should have fun, regardless of their <u>physical</u> abilities.

What does the word <u>physical</u> mean?

A Friendly

B Related to school

C Entertaining

D Related to the body

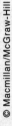

10 Why is the title "A Dream Comes True" a good title for this article? Explain your answer and support it with details from the article.

_____

_____

_____

_____

_____

_____

BE SURE YOU HAVE RECORDED ALL OF YOUR ANSWERS
ON THE ANSWER DOCUMENT.

Weslandia

Use this selection to answer questions 1–10.

---

1 What happens to Wesley at the beginning of the story?

  A He shaves his head to fit in with his classmates.

  B He is teased and chased by his classmates.

  C He does what his parents ask him to do.

  D He eats pizza and drinks soda.

3 What finally grows in Wesley's garden?

  A Weeds that grow up to his knees

  B Tomatoes, beans, and Brussels sprouts

  C Magenta fruit with a purple center

  D Peaches, strawberries, and pumpkins

2 What does Wesley decide to do for his summer project?

  F Help his parents grow food in their garden

  G Create his own way of life

  H Make friends with the neighborhood boys

  J Read about ancient ways of life

4 What does Wesley do in Weslandia?

  F He creates his own school.

  G He watches his friends play games.

  H He reads books and writes stories.

  J He invents new food, games, and clothing.

5 How does Wesley change by the end of the story?

   A He makes a lot of friends.

   B He starts cutting his hair.

   C He begins to enjoy football.

   D He starts to like pizza.

6 What does the conversation between Wesley and his neighbor reveal about Wesley?

   F He does not do what is expected of him.

   G He doesn't know how to care for a garden.

   H He does not take help when it is offered to him.

   J He doesn't have good relationships with other people.

7 Read this sentence.

He used the ink and his own eighty-letter alphabet to record the history of his civilization's founding.

In this sentence, the word founding means —

   A achievements

   B beginning

   C ending

   D growth

GO ON

8 Read this sentence.

As the <u>finale</u> to his summer project, he wrote a history.

The word <u>finale</u> comes from a root that means —

  F end

  G neighbor

  H love

  J sport

9 Read this sentence from the story.

He had no <u>shortage</u> of friends.

Which word means the same as <u>shortage</u>?

  A Amount

  B Lack

  C Problem

  D Welcome

GO ON ➡

10 What is the theme or message in this story? Explain your answer and support it with details from the story.

_____

_____

_____

_____

_____

_____

_____

BE SURE YOU HAVE RECORDED ALL OF YOUR ANSWERS
ON THE ANSWER DOCUMENT.

Selection Test

The Gri Gri Tree

Use this selection to answer questions 1–10.

1 Why do the people think the narrator is strange?

    A She makes up wild stories.

    B She spends most of her time up in a tree.

    C She counts roses in the neighbor's yard.

    D She likes watching sea monsters.

2 Why are the people worried when they hear about the sea monster?

    F They think it will harm their children.

    G They think it will scare people away from their island.

    H They think they will run out of food.

    J They think they will no longer be able to swim in the ocean.

3 What does Mami propose to do to about the sea monster?

    A She thinks the people of the village should scare it away.

    B She decides that the sea monster should be kept a secret.

    C She wants to make a sign about the sea monster.

    D She wants the narrator to write a story about it.

4 How does the narrator feel about Guario?

    F She wants to help him succeed.

    G She looks up to him.

    H She likes to compete with him.

    J She thinks he is too serious.

5 The way the people feel about the narrator changes when she —

A sees the sea monster

B sits in the gri gri tree

C reads her story aloud

D hugs her brother Guario

6 Why is the gri gri tree a special place for the narrator?

F She can avoid doing chores in the tree.

G She can imagine anything she wants in the tree.

H She can fall asleep in the tree.

J She can practice writing in the tree.

7 Read this sentence from the story.

That was more than anyone else had ventured to <u>inquire</u>.

The word <u>inquire</u> comes from a root that means —

A learn

B ask

C understand

D wish

GO ON

Selection Test

8 Read this sentence.

A black shape <u>emerged</u> from the fountain of water.

What does the word <u>emerged</u> mean?

F Came out

G Made a noise

H Started laughing

J Looked closely

9 Read this sentence.

The children <u>sprawled</u> on the floor.

The word <u>sprawled</u> means —

A ran around in a circle

B spread out carelessly

C fell asleep

D stood in a straight line

10 What happens to the narrator in this story? Write a summary telling what happens.

_____

_____

_____

_____

_____

_____

BE SURE YOU HAVE RECORDED ALL OF YOUR ANSWERS ON THE ANSWER DOCUMENT.

Weekly Assessment

Macmillan/McGraw-Hill

Student Name _____

Date _____

Weekly Assessment

TESTED SKILLS AND STRATEGIES

- **Reading Comprehension**
- **Vocabulary Strategies**
- **Spelling**
- **Grammar, Mechanics, and Usage**

Mc Graw Hill **Macmillan/McGraw-Hill**

Six Brave Students

1   September 15, 1958, was not an ordinary day for Cathy Washington and five other children in Tennessee. On this day they would become the first African American students to attend the Bluebell Lane School.

2   It was a spectacular day, with the sun shining brightly in a clear blue sky. "At least the weather is on our side," said Cathy to her companions. They laughed feebly. But they recognized the dangerous battle they were facing to obtain their right to an education.

3   The children got on the public bus and paid their fares. On the route to school, they saw many angry people lined up in the street. The protesters raised tightly clenched fists. "Go home!" they yelled. "We don't want you here. Go back to your own school on your side of town."

4   "We belong here," Cathy blurted out, even though the people on the street couldn't hear her. Then she calmed down a bit and said, "Four years ago, the Supreme Court said that we can get an education with white

Page 2

GO ON ➤

students. We don't need your permission to attend your school because it's our school as well." She spoke as if she were practicing something that she planned to say to a crowd of people.

5   Cathy's friend Tyrone eyed the other passengers and said nervously, "Cathy, stop talking. We don't want to do anything that might cause even more trouble. I feel enough trouble in the air already."

6   At the school, a mob of people yelled. A few threw rotten pieces of fruit. Police officers tried to keep the peace. Although Cathy and the other children were fearful, they did not show it, and they certainly did not change their minds about the historic action they were about to take. As they approached the school entrance, Cathy glanced at the words over the door. She read aloud the school motto that was chiseled in stone. "With equality for all," it said.

7   The six African American students held their heads high as they walked into the building. All of them knew that this was only the beginning of the battle. They also realized that while some white students would become their friends, others never would.

8   Those six students persevered and completed their education at the Bluebell Lane School. Many years later, one of their former classmates asked Cathy for her autograph.

9   "Why do you want my signature?" Cathy asked the white woman.

10   "Because I admire your courage," the woman replied. "You were only a child, but you stood up for your rights on that sunny day in September. I've been a teacher for 15 years, Cathy. And by now I've told hundreds of students about what you did at that school. For them, you're a hero."

1 Which words best describe Cathy's character?

  A Shy and modest

  B Angry and defiant

  C Nervous and fearful

  D Brave and confident

2 Which detail is part of the setting of this story?

  F A mob of people yelled.

  G Six students completed their education.

  H A child stood up for her rights.

  J The children got on the public bus.

3 Which word best describes Tyrone?

  A Bossy

  B Calm

  C Cautious

  D Outspoken

4 What does the reader learn about Cathy based on the question she asks at the end of the story?

  F She likes to look back at the past.

  G She remains angry about what happened.

  H She does not like being asked for her autograph.

  J She may not realize the importance of what she did.

GO ON

5 In paragraph 2, the word spectacular means —

A new

B interesting

C proud

D wonderful

6 Which word is pronounced the same as the word <u>fare</u> in paragraph 3?

F Fear

G Fair

H Far

J Fur

7 In paragraph 3, what does the word <u>clenched</u> mean?

A Closed

B Strong

C Relaxed

D Large

8 In paragraph 6, the word <u>approached</u> means —

F came nearer to

G began to work on

H looked closely

J hurried past

9 Why do the protesters react the way they do when the African American students go to the school? Explain your answer and support it with details from the story.

_____

_____

_____

_____

_____

_____

Page 5

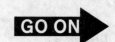

DIRECTIONS

Read the introduction and the passage that follows. Then read each question and fill in the correct answer on your answer sheet.

Cecilia wrote this story about her life. She wants you to review her paper. As you read, think about the corrections and improvements that Cecilia should make. Then answer the questions that follow.

My Life

(1) I was born in a Colorado town in the mountains? (2) My mom and dad say that it was a beautiful place, but I don't remember it. (3) I was one year old when we moved to Freeport. (4) On the Gulf Coast of Texas. (5) My mom and dad don't like Freeport's heat and dampe air. (6) They complain about it I tell them that complaining doesn't do any good. (7) I like Freeport's beaches. (8) The sand feels ruff between my toes, and the water is cool.

GO ON ▶

10 What change, if any, should be made in sentence 1?

  F Change the question mark to a period

  G Insert a comma after *town*

  H Change *was* to **were**

  J Make no change

11 What is the **BEST** way to combine sentences 3 and 4?

  A On the Gulf Coast of Texas, I was one year old when we moved to Freeport.

  B I was one year old on the Gulf Coast of Texas when we moved to Freeport.

  C I was one year old when we moved to Freeport, on the Gulf Coast of Texas.

  D When we moved to Freeport, I was one year old on the Gulf Coast of Texas.

12 What change, if any, should be made in sentence 5?

  F Change *My* to **Mine**

  G Change *don't* to **do'nt**

  H Change *dampe* to **damp**

  J Make no change

13 What revision, if any, is needed in sentence 6?

  A They complain about it, then I tell them that complaining doesn't do any good.

  B They complain that it doesn't do any good, and I tell them that complaining.

  C They complain about it, but I tell them that complaining doesn't do any good.

  D No revision is needed.

14 What change, if any, should be made in sentence 8?

  F Change the period to an exclamation point

  G Change *ruff* to **rough**

  H Change *toes* to **toe**

  J Make no change

BE SURE YOU HAVE RECORDED ALL OF YOUR ANSWERS ON THE ANSWER DOCUMENT.

STOP

Grade 5 • Unit 1 • Week 1
Student Evaluation Chart

Tested Skills	Number Correct	Percent Correct
Reading Comprehension: *Character and Setting,* 1, 2, 3, 4	/4	%
Short Answer: *Character and Setting,* 9	/3	%
Vocabulary Strategies: *Context Clues,* 5, 7, 8; *Context Clues: Homophones,* 6	/4	%
Spelling: *Words with Short Vowels,* 12, 14	/2	%
Grammar, Mechanics, and Usage: *Punctuate Sentences,* 10; *Sentences,* 11, 13	/3	%
Total Weekly Test Score	/16	%

Student Name _____

Date _____

Weekly Assessment

TESTED SKILLS AND STRATEGIES

- **Reading Comprehension**
- **Vocabulary Strategies**
- **Spelling**
- **Grammar, Mechanics, and Usage**

Macmillan/McGraw-Hill

Something to Do

1   Ever since school let out for the summer, Kyle O'Hara had been spending his afternoons watching TV and slurping soda. His dad would warn him to turn off the TV set now and then. Each time Kyle would protest, and his dad would reply, "I'm not sorry. I'd have more <u>sympathy</u> for you if you worked as hard as I do!"

2   One afternoon Kyle lingered in the lobby of his apartment building, feeling mournful. Mr. Jackson, the custodian for the building, stopped to chat and find out what was wrong. At first Kyle didn't want to admit how bored he was. But he considered Mr. Jackson a friend, and finally he told him.

3   The custodian thought about Kyle's problem for a moment. "Well," he began, "several elderly residents in this building can't get outside much anymore. Maybe you could run errands for them."

4   "That's a great idea!" exclaimed Kyle. Later that afternoon Kyle posted a flyer on the bulletin board in the lobby and told his father about his plan. Days went by, and he didn't receive a single phone call in response to the flyer. He found this bewildering. In the flyer he had listed really low prices for his services. One day Kyle left his apartment in search of Mr. Jackson.

© Macmillan/McGraw-Hill

GO ON ➡

The custodian was delivering a package to a resident. Kyle told him he had not received any phone calls.

5   "That's strange," Mr. Jackson told Kyle. "I know that Mrs. Kim's dog needs exercise, but she can't walk him. And Mr. Castelli has an <u>injury</u>, so it is hard for him to get around. He needs someone to pick up his prescriptions. Maybe they just don't have money to spare."

6   Kyle could hardly believe his ears. He simply couldn't associate his building's luxurious apartments and fancy lobby with people who were struggling to make ends meet.

7   Mr. Jackson must have read his mind. He said, "Some of the residents have lived in this building a long time. It's hard to pay rent that keeps going up when your income stays the same."

8   Kyle hesitated and then said, "You know, I'm mainly looking for something to keep me busy until school starts. The pay isn't the main consideration for me."

9   "It is for them, Kyle," Mr. Jackson said.

10   Kyle understood what he meant. He rode the elevator to the third floor, walked down the hall, and knocked on a door. Mrs. Kim opened it. But before she could say anything, Kyle asked, "Would you like me to walk your dog? There's no charge."

11   A little dog peeked at Kyle from around the door. "Oh, Kyle!" said Mrs. Kim. "That would be so nice. Trixie is a little shy, but she'll take to you quickly. And maybe in the future I can find a way to return the favor."

12   As Trixie bounded down the street ahead of Kyle, he made sure to keep a tight grip on her leash. When they rounded the corner, they passed Kyle's father, who was on his way home from work. He gave Kyle a broad grin as he walked by.

© Macmillan/McGraw-Hill

Page 3

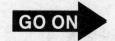

1 What can the reader conclude about Kyle's father in this story?

A He does not like to spend time with Kyle.

B He never takes time out to have fun.

C He wants Kyle to use his time wisely.

D He wants to get rid of the television set.

2 Which statement is most likely true about Mr. Jackson?

F He is too busy to think of others.

G He wants all young people to get a job.

H He understands how to help people.

J He does not believe Kyle is very responsible.

3 At the end of the story, the reader can tell that Mr. O'Hara —

A is confused because he knows Kyle does not have a dog

B is angry because he thinks Kyle got a dog without permission

C is pleased to see that Kyle is doing something worthwhile

D is surprised because he didn't know Kyle had a dog

4 How will Kyle probably spend the rest of his summer afternoons?

F Playing with people's dogs in the park

G Sitting in front of the television set

H Helping the elderly people in his building

J Working at his father's office

GO ON

Page 4

5 In paragraph 1, the word
  <u>sympathy</u> means —

  A time

  B respect

  C interest

  D understanding

6 In paragraph 5, what does the
  word <u>injury</u> mean?

  F Harm or damage

  G Thought or belief

  H Long distance

  J Person who helps

7 In paragraph 6, the phrase "make
  ends meet" means —

  A come to the end

  B make a connection

  C reach an agreement

  D have enough money

8 In paragraph 11, what does the
  phrase "take to you" mean?

  F Look shyly at

  G Get used to

  H Run away from

  J Be patient with

9 How does Mr. Jackson most likely influence Kyle? Explain your answer and
  support it with details from the story.

_____

_____

_____

_____

_____

_____

GO ON

Page 5

DIRECTIONS

Read the introduction and the passage that follows. Then read each question and fill in the correct answer on your answer document.

Rosalie wrote this draft of an article. The article contains errors. As you read, think about the corrections and improvements that Rosalie should make. Then answer the questions that follow.

Holidays

(1) You'll see many holidays named on any tipe of calendar used in the United States. (2) Some of them are celebrated for religious reasons, and others are celebrated for historical reasons. (3) Independence Day, July 4th is probably the most important historical holiday. (4) On this day, Americans celebrate the declaration of our country's independence from England. (5) Is another historical holiday. (6) On this day, fokes remember the Pilgrims' first harvest. (7) It is celebrated on the fourth Thursday in November. (8) Other important holidays include Labor Day Memorial Day and New Year's Day.

GO ON ➡

Page 6

10 What change, if any, should be made in sentence 1?

  F Change *You'll* to **Youl'l**

  G Change *tipe* to **type**

  H Change *United States* to **United states**

  J Make no change

11 What change, if any, should be made to sentence 3?

  A Change the period to a question mark

  B Change *celebrated* to **selebrated**

  C Insert a comma after *July 4th*

  D Make no change

12 What revision, if any, is needed in sentence 5?

  F Thanksgiving, another historical holiday.

  G Another historical holiday is.

  H Thanksgiving is another historical holiday.

  J No revision is needed.

13 What change, if any, should be made in sentence 6?

  A Change *fokes* to **folks**

  B Change *Pilgrims'* to **Pilgrims**

  C Change *first* to **ferst**

  D Make no change

14 What is the **BEST** way to rewrite sentence 8?

  F Other important holidays include, Labor Day, Memorial Day and New Year's Day.

  G Other important holidays include; Labor Day Memorial Day and New Year's Day.

  H Other important holidays include Labor Day, Memorial Day, and New Year's Day.

  J Other important holidays include Labor Day; Memorial Day; and New Year's Day.

© Macmillan/McGraw-Hill

Page 7

BE SURE YOU HAVE RECORDED ALL OF YOUR ANSWERS ON THE ANSWER DOCUMENT.

Grade 5 • Unit 1 • Week 2
Student Evaluation Chart

Tested Skills	Number Correct	Percent Correct
Reading Comprehension: *Make Inferences,* 1, 2, 3, 4	/4	%
Short Answer: *Make Inferences,* 9	/3	%
Vocabulary Strategies: *Context Clues,* 5, 6; *Dictionary: Idioms and Adages,* 7, 8	/4	%
Spelling: *Words with Long Vowels,* 10, 13	/2	%
Grammar, Mechanics, and Usage: *Commas in Appositives,* 11; *Subject and Predicate,* 12; *Commas in a Series,* 14	/3	%
Total Weekly Test Score	/16	%

Student Name _____

Date _____

Weekly Assessment

TESTED SKILLS AND STRATEGIES

- **Reading Comprehension**
- **Vocabulary Strategies**
- **Spelling**
- **Grammar, Mechanics, and Usage**

Mc Graw Hill **Macmillan/McGraw-Hill**

Life in the Middle Ages

1   The Middle Ages began more than 1,000 years ago and lasted about 500 years. This period is called the Middle Ages because it occurred between ancient and modern times.

2   People in the Middle Ages lived in a social system in which there were strict divisions between social classes. Each social class was based on the kinds of jobs people held and their level of wealth. Because there was no equality in this system, people from different social classes were treated in very different ways. The kings and queens were the most powerful people. They owned most of the land and were considered the upper class. The people who worked for the church were almost as powerful as the royalty. Then came the professionals, such as doctors, lawyers, bankers, merchants, and skilled trades people, who made up the middle class.

3   The upper class owned the land, but the lower class worked it. The farmers who worked the land were very poor and had very little power. They made up the lower class. They did not own their land or their homes, and they worked for the landowners. In turn, the landowners usually gave them protection from thieves and invading armies.

4   Education in the Middle Ages was mainly for young people from wealthy families. Of the girls who were educated, most studied in their own homes or in the homes of other wealthy families. Most of them

GO ON

learned the skills needed to manage a household, and some also learned to sing or play musical instruments. Most boys went to schools run by the church. Boys did not study what you study today. Back then, they learned only reading, writing, and some math. Most of the young people who got an education planned to enter religious life.

5   There also was a different kind of education in the Middle Ages. Between the ages of seven and twelve, some children learned by working with people who had already mastered trades or crafts. The students worked in stores or workshops with the masters. Some young people <u>dedicated</u> seven years to learning a trade or craft. At the end of that time, they could open their own workshops or stores. The number of young people who studied or learned a trade or craft was small, however. Most children did not get an education at all. They went right to work at an early age.

6   How do we know so much about the Middle Ages? Historians learn about the past from several sources. They read the writings of people who lived during a certain period. They carefully examine paintings, drawings, and other types of art created during the period. They also learn about the past from <u>artifacts</u>. These are objects made by people at some point in history. Artifacts might be tools, household items, or clothing. Often the artifacts are found at the <u>site</u> where they were used, such as a home, church, or workshop. Many of these items are now in museum exhibits.

1 What is this article mainly about?

A Farmers in the Middle Ages

B Differences between trades and crafts

C How people lived in the Middle Ages

D Looking for artifacts from the Middle Ages

2 Which word from paragraph 2 is a plural form of a noun?

F *System*

G *Level*

H *Wealth*

J *Classes*

Page 3

3 Look at the web of information from the article.

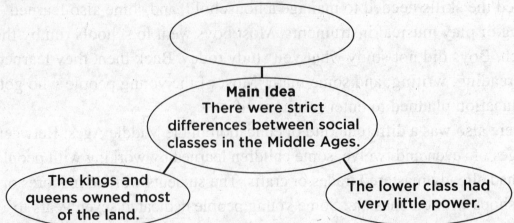

Main Idea
There were strict differences between social classes in the Middle Ages.

The kings and queens owned most of the land.

The lower class had very little power.

Which of the following belongs in the empty oval?

A Girls did not go to school because they studied at home.

B Professionals made up the middle class.

C Boys learned reading, writing, and math.

D Artifacts tell historians a lot about the Middle Ages.

4 Which detail supports the idea that education in the Middle Ages was different from education today?

F Children in those days learned to sing.

G Girls were only educated in their homes.

H Boys learned reading and writing.

J Children went to school early in the day.

5 In paragraph 5, the word dedicated means —

A gave or committed

B refused

C made or created

D found

© Macmillan/McGraw-Hill

GO ON

Page 4

6 Why did farmers have very little power during the Middle Ages?

    F Most children went to work in the fields at an early age.

    G Social class was based on the work people did and on their wealth.

    H Between the ages of seven and twelve, some children learned trades or crafts.

    J Landowners usually gave farmers protection from thieves and invading armies.

7 In paragraph 6, what does the word artifacts mean?

    A People of long ago

    B Bright colors

    C Objects from history

    D Difficult tasks

8 Which word means the same as site?

    F Class

    G Place

    H Art

    J Period

9 How have historians learned so much about the Middle Ages? Explain your answer and support it with details from the article.

_____

_____

_____

_____

_____

_____

© Macmillan/McGraw-Hill

GO ON

DIRECTIONS

Read the introduction and the passage that follows. Then read each question and fill in the correct answer on your answer document.

Michelle wrote this story about a man named Jacob. She wants you to review her paper. As you read, think about the corrections and improvements that Michelle should make. Then answer the questions that follow.

Reaching the Top

(1) Jacob reached the top of the mountain and looked at the amazing view of the countryside. (2) He couldn't believe he had finally made it to the summit. (3) He stretched out his arms and breathed deeply. (4) He took a sip of water. (5) He admired the scenery. (6) The sky was a deep hugh of blue. (7) He knew he needed to rest for a while there was a flat, grassy spot nearby. (8) He pulled out a light tarp and he lay down in the sun. (9) Soon he was asleep.

GO ON

Weekly Assessment

10 What change, if any, should be made in sentence 1?

  F Change *view* to **veiw**

  G Change *countryside* to **country side**

  H Insert a comma after *mountain*

  J Make no change

11 What is the **BEST** way to combine sentences 4 and 5?

  A He admired and sipped the cool scenery and water.

  B He took a sip of water while he admired the scenery.

  C A sip of water he took, as he admired the scenery.

  D The scenery he admired, he took a sip of water.

12 What change, if any, should be made to sentence 6?

  F Change *sky* to **skye**

  G Change *hugh* to **hue**

  H Insert a comma after *deep*

  J Make no change

13 What revision, if any, is needed in sentence 7?

  A He knew he needed to rest for a while, and there was a flat, grassy spot nearby.

  B He knew he needed to rest for a while, there was a flat, grassy spot nearby.

  C He knew he needed to rest for a while but there was a flat, grassy spot nearby.

  D No revision is needed.

14 What is the **BEST** way to rewrite sentence 8?

  F He pulled out a light tarp, lay down in the sun.

  G He pulled out a light tarp and, he lay down in the sun.

  H He pulled out a light tarp, and he lay down in the sun.

  J He pulled out a light tarp, in the sun, and lay down.

BE SURE YOU HAVE RECORDED ALL OF YOUR ANSWERS ON THE ANSWER DOCUMENT.

Grade 5 • Unit 1 • Week 3
Student Evaluation Chart

Tested Skills	Number Correct	Percent Correct
Reading Comprehension: *Main Idea and Details*, 1, 3, 4, 6	/4	%
Short Answer: *Main Idea and Details*, 9	/3	%
Vocabulary Strategies: *Word Parts: Inflectional Endings*, 2; *Context Clues*, 5, 7, 8	/4	%
Spelling: *Words with /ū/, /ů/, /ü/*, 10, 12	/2	%
Grammar, Mechanics, and Usage: *Sentence Combining*, 11; *Punctuating Compound Sentences*, 13, 14	/3	%
Total Weekly Test Score	/16	%

Student Name _____

Date _____

Weekly Assessment

TESTED SKILLS AND STRATEGIES

- **Reading Comprehension**
- **Vocabulary Strategies**
- **Spelling**
- **Grammar, Mechanics, and Usage**

Mc Graw Hill Macmillan/McGraw-Hill

A Carnival Costume

1   Marisol lived on the Caribbean island of Trinidad, and Carnival was approaching. It was a celebration filled with parades, dances, and music, and almost everyone on the island would join the fun. But Marisol had a problem: How could she get a costume for it? "Carnival is so special," she said to her friend Nicolette one day. "I really want to wear a beautiful costume that everyone will notice."

2   "Do you want an elegant costume?" Nicolette asked.

3   "Well, that would be irresistible. Who could turn that down?" Marisol said. "But I'm reluctant to ask my parents because a fancy costume costs a lot of money."

4   "Why don't we make you a costume?" Nicolette suggested.

5   "We don't know how to sew," Marisol replied.

6   "That won't be a problem," Nicolette assured her. The girls went to Marisol's house and sewed fabric scraps together. As they worked, they gossiped about the people in their neighborhood. They shared rumors they had heard about everyone.

7   When the costume was finished, Marisol tried it on. "It's ugly," she said, "and it doesn't fit me right."

© Macmillan/McGraw-Hill

GO ON

Page 2

8   "You're right, it's horrible," Nicolette agreed. "What can we do now?"

9   "Let's ask your grandmother to help us," Marisol said. "She makes beautiful costumes." But the girls knew that Mrs. Blanco would be very busy making costumes for Carnival.

10   Nicolette and Marisol walked to Mrs. Blanco's store. It was filled with customers and <u>mischievous</u> kids running in and out of the racks of brightly colored skirts and tops. The kids' mothers told them, "You must stop. Running like that is <u>forbidden</u> in Mrs. Blanco's store." But the kids giggled and continued to run.

11   Nicolette explained Marisol's problem to her grandmother. Mrs. Blanco said, "I'd like to help you, Marisol, but I have too much work to do. This is my busiest season of the year."

12   "Grandmother, what if we help you by cleaning the store?" Nicolette asked.

13   "And we can run errands for you. And we'll do anything else you need to have done," Marisol added.

14   Mrs. Blanco thought for a few seconds and then she said, "All right, girls. If you help me, then I'll have time to make Marisol's costume."

15   On the morning of Carnival Tuesday, Mrs. Blanco gave Marisol her costume. It was beautiful.

16   "Thank you! Thank you!" Marisol told Mrs. Blanco and hugged her.

17   The music blared loudly in the streets, The two girls walked toward the group they planned to join in the parade. Marisol's costume shimmered in the bright Caribbean sunlight. "I feel like a princess," she told Nicolette.

18   "You look like a princess, too, thanks to my grandmother," said Nicolette.

19   "She's your grandmother, and she's my fairy godmother," Marisol said with a smile.

Page 3

GO ON

1 Look at the diagram of information from the story.

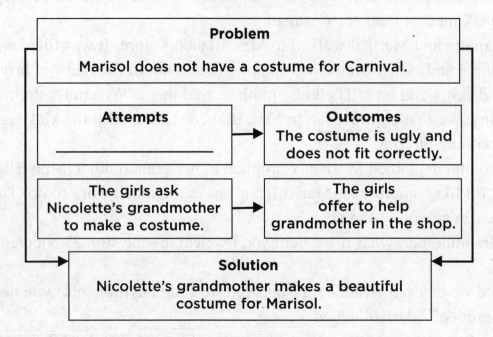

Which of the following belongs on the blank line?

A Marisol and Nicolette ask for some money.

B Marisol and Nicolette look for a cheap costume in a store.

C Marisol and Nicolette try to make a costume.

D Marisol and Nicolette borrow a costume from Marisol's parents.

2 In the beginning of the story, Marisol does not have a costume for Carnival because —

F costumes are too expensive

G her parents refuse to make one

H she is too young to own a costume

J the costume was lost last year

3 The girls' first costume did not turn out well because they did not —

A have enough fabric

B use the correct needle

C have enough time

D know how to sew

Page 4

GO ON

4 At first, why won't Nicolette's grandmother make a costume for Marisol?

F She wants to make one for Nicolette instead.

G She is annoyed that the girls are running around in her store.

H She is too busy and does not have enough time.

J She has used all her fabric for the customers in her store.

5 In paragraph 3, what does the word irresistible mean?

A Easy to resist

B Not able to be resisted

C One who resists

D Resisted before

6 In paragraph 6, gossiped means —

F argued

G talked loudly

H told stories about others

J spoke seriously to each other

7 In paragraph 10, the word mischievous means —

A full of mischief

B without mischief

C one who hates mischief

D unable to do mischief

8 In paragraph 10, forbidden means —

F expected

G not usual

H dangerous

J not allowed

9 How are Marisol and Nicolette good problem solvers? Explain your answer and support it with details from the story.

_____

_____

_____

_____

GO ON

Page 5

DIRECTIONS

Read the introduction and the passage that follows. Then read each question and fill in the correct answer on your answer document.

Victor wrote this article about nuts. He wants you to review his paper. As you read, think about the corrections and improvements that Victor should make. Then answer the questions that follow.

Nuts About Nuts

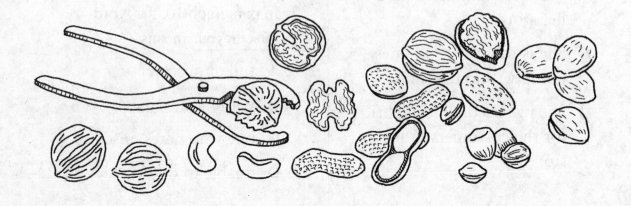

(1) Many people believe that eating nuts is not good for your health. (2) However, many doctors, including dr. Jones, from the Main Street Clinic, think that eating nuts can help keep your body healthy. (3) Even though nuts do contain a lot of fat, most of this fat is healthy fat. (4) Eating nuts is also important because they are a good sourse of fiber. (5) Fiber is important because it helps lower your cholesterol and keeps your heart healthy. (6) Nuts have a lot of calories. (7) Eat only a few at a time. (8) It is also important to avoid eating nuts covered in sugar or salt. (9) You will cancel out the health benefits.

GO ON ➡

Page 6

Student Name _____

10 What change, if any, should be made in sentence 2?

   F Change *dr.* to **Dr.**

   G Delete the comma after *however*

   H Place a colon after *that*

   J Make no change

11 What change, if any, should be made in sentence 4?

   A Change *sourse* to **source**

   B Change *they* to **them**

   C Insert a comma after *important*

   D Make no change

12 What change, if any, should be made in sentence 5?

   F Change *heart* to **hart**

   G Change *helps* to **help**

   H Insert a comma after *cholesterol*

   J Make no change

13 What is the **BEST** way to combine sentences 6 and 7?

   A Nuts have, a lot of calories, eat only a few at a time.

   B Nuts have a lot of calories, and eat only a few, at a time.

   C Nuts have a lot of calories, a few at a time, eat only.

   D Nuts have a lot of calories, so eat only a few at a time.

14 What is the **BEST** way to combine sentences 8 and 9?

   F It is also important to avoid eating nuts covered in sugar or salt because you will cancel out the health benefits.

   G It is also important to avoid eating nuts covered in sugar or salt, you will cancel out the health benefits.

   H It is also important to avoid eating nuts covered in sugar or salt, but you will cancel out the health benefits.

   J It is also important to avoid eating nuts covered in sugar or salt, will cancel out the health benefits.

BE SURE YOU HAVE RECORDED ALL OF YOUR ANSWERS ON THE ANSWER DOCUMENT.

Grade 5 • Unit 1 • Week 4
Student Evaluation Chart

Tested Skills	Number Correct	Percent Correct
Reading Comprehension: *Problem and Solution*, 1, 2, 3, 4	/4	%
Short Answer: *Problem and Solution*, 9	/3	%
Vocabulary Strategies: *Word Parts: Suffixes*, 5, 7; *Context Clues*, 6, 8	/4	%
Spelling: *Words with r-controlled vowels /är/, /âr/, /ôr/* 11, 12	/2	%
Grammar, Mechanics, and Usage: *Commas, Colons, and Capital Letters*, 10; *Sentence Combining/ Complex Sentences*, 13, 14	/3	%
Total Weekly Test Score	/16	%

Student Name _____

Date _____

Weekly Assessment

TESTED SKILLS AND STRATEGIES

- **Reading Comprehension**
- **Vocabulary Strategies**
- **Spelling**
- **Grammar, Mechanics, and Usage**

A Spy in the American Revolution

1   "It's too dangerous, William. I can't allow you to do this," Mrs. Sommers said. She rubbed her hands together nervously.

2   "Ma, I'm 12 years old, and that is old enough. I want to support our soldiers in their fight against that tyrant, King George. I want to help the Colonies become independent from Great Britain and its tyranny."

3   "William does have spunk," his older sister Mercy said. "Remember how he stood up to the Redcoats? Thanks to William's bravery, we were able to protect our animals."

4   Mr. Sommers spoke up. "William is good at navigation and can find his way anywhere. And he learns quickly. People will be able to instruct him on how to help our cause."

5   The family continued discussing the matter through the night. By dawn, Mr. and Mrs. Sommers had agreed to let their son spy for the American Colonies. They knew he would bring important information to the local leaders of the Revolution.

6   William rested for a while. Then he ate a warm meal, hugged his parents, and set off. He soon found the stark British camp. With a confident swagger, he walked boldly into the camp. The soldiers took no notice of him.

© Macmillan/McGraw-Hill

GO ON

7   William made a careful observation of the camp. He estimated that there were several hundred men. He saw cannons everywhere. He noticed that the British had a lot of flour and dried beef. "We could use those supplies," he thought. He also listened to the men talking. He overheard one of the captains say that horses were being prepared. The troops were planning to set out that night. Some of the troops had already left. They were going to attack the patriots!

8   That evening William stole away from the British camp. A few hours later he was reporting to the patriots what he had seen and heard among the British. "You're quite brave, boy," one of the colonial soldiers said. "Now we know when the enemy plans to attack and how well prepared they are."

9   William went on many other spy missions. At times the information he brought to the patriots was extremely important. At other times it was less helpful. But at the end of every mission they praised him for his daring and his efforts.

10   When he returned from his final mission, his father told him, "What a wonderful thing you've done for America, son." His father rarely gave compliments, and this remark made William beam.

11   A few years later, after the patriots had won their cause, the governor of New Jersey gave William a medal for his work as a spy. Decades later, when William was an old man, he loved telling his grandchildren about the important part he had played in the American Revolution.

Page 3

GO ON

1 Why did the governor of New Jersey award a medal to William?

   A William overheard the captain say that horses had been prepared.

   B William walked with a confident swagger into the British camp.

   C William was a daring spy who helped the American colonies.

   D William had great memories about his role in the Revolution.

2 What is the most likely reason that William is able to gather so much information?

   F He is lucky and has a lot of help.

   G His father taught him how to be a spy.

   H The British soldiers want to brag about their plans to him.

   J The British soldiers do not notice him because he is young.

3 All of the other members of William's family are —

   A loyal to the Colonies

   B not sure William is old enough to be a spy

   C secretly supporting the British in the war

   D working as spies for the patriots

4 How does William know his father is proud of him?

   F He gives William a medal of honor.

   G He offers to pay William for his services.

   H He praises William for a job well done.

   J He asks the soldiers if William can keep spying.

GO ON ➡

5 Which word from the story is in the same word family as <u>tyrant</u> in paragraph 2?

   A *troops*

   B *tyranny*

   C *matter*

   D *daring*

6 In paragraph 4, the word <u>instruct</u> means —

   F watch

   G advise

   H correct

   J repeat

7 In paragraph 4, the word <u>navigation</u> means —

   A the process of finding the way

   B a person who finds the way

   C not able to find the way

   D after finding the way

8 Which word is in the same word family as <u>patriots</u> in paragraph 7?

   F Praised

   G Patriotism

   H Patrolman

   J Prepared

9 How can the reader tell that William is proud of his role in the American Revolution? Explain your answer and support it with details from the story.

_____

_____

_____

_____

_____

GO ON

Page 5

DIRECTIONS

Read the introduction and the passage that follows. Then read each question and fill in the correct answer on your answer document.

Karl wrote this story in his journal. He wants you to review his paper. As you read, think about the corrections and improvements that Karl should make. Then answer the questions that follow.

Baseball Basics

(1) My favorite sport is baseball, even though I have only been on a team for one yeer. (2) I know a lot about this sport. (3) Nine players in the field at one time. (4) Three players are in the outfield ready to catch fly balls, there are four players in the infield. (5) The pitcher and the catcher make up the rest of the team. (6) My favorite part of the game is when I hit a home run and get to clear the bases. (7) I do not like to pitch because it is very hard you have to throw the ball perfectly so batters can't hit it.

GO ON

10 What change, if any, should be made in sentence 1?

   F Change *is* to **are**

   G Change *I have* to **I'll**

   H Change *yeer* to **year**

   J Make no change

11 What revision, if any, is needed in sentence 3?

   A There are nine players on the field at one time.

   B Only nine players on the field at one time.

   C At one time, nine players on the field.

   D No revision is needed.

12 What change, if any, is needed in sentence 4?

   F Change *three* to **3**

   G Change *infield* to **Infield**

   H Insert **and** before *there*

   J Make no change

13 What change, if any, should be made in sentence 6?

   A Insert a comma before *and*

   B Change *clear* to **cleer**

   C Change the period to a question mark

   D Make no change

14 What revision, if any, is needed in sentence 7?

   F I do not like to pitch because it is very hard, you have to throw the ball perfectly so batters can't hit it.

   G I do not like to pitch because it is very hard. You have to throw the ball perfectly so batters can't hit it.

   H I do not like to pitch because it is very hard because you have to throw the ball perfectly so batters can't hit it.

   J No revision is needed.

Page 7

BE SURE YOU HAVE RECORDED ALL OF YOUR ANSWERS ON THE ANSWER DOCUMENT.

STOP

Student Name _____

Grade 5 • Unit 1 • Week 5
Student Evaluation Chart

Tested Skills	Number Correct	Percent Correct
Reading Comprehension: *Draw Conclusions*, 1, 2, 4; *Make Inferences*, 3	/4	%
Short Answer: *Draw Conclusions*, 9	/3	%
Vocabulary Strategies: *Context Clues*, 5; *Word Families*, 6, 8; *Word Parts: Suffixes*, 7	/4	%
Spelling: *Words with r-controlled vowels* er, ir, ur, 10, 13	/2	%
Grammar, Mechanics, and Usage: *Correcting Fragments*, 11; *Run-on Sentences*, 12, 14	/3	%
Total Weekly Test Score	/16	%

Student Name _____

Date _____

Weekly Assessment

TESTED SKILLS AND STRATEGIES

- **Reading Comprehension**
- **Vocabulary Strategies**
- **Spelling**
- **Grammar, Mechanics, and Usage**

Macmillan/McGraw-Hill

Valuable Plants

1   In the early 1800s, two men named Lewis and Clark explored the American West. They started from St. Louis in May 1804 and traveled northwest up the Missouri River. By winter of that year, they had reached the Dakotas, where they met a Native American girl named Sacagawea. At the age of 16, Sacagawea joined the two explorers and traveled with them as a guide. Together, they scoured the areas along the Missouri River and into the Rocky Mountains, hoping to make new discoveries. Sacagawea knew a great deal about the land, and she shared her knowledge with Lewis and Clark. By November 1805, the explorers had crossed the Rocky Mountains and reached the Pacific Ocean.

2   One of Lewis and Clark's goals was to collect different types of plants. Sacagawea helped the explorers learn about the specimens they collected. She taught them that nature could cure common illnesses. She identified plants that could be used as foods and medicines. She prepared the plants in cakes and teas that were both healthful and had healing power.

3   Sacagawea showed Lewis and Clark a plant called Indian Bread Root. It could be peeled and eaten raw or pounded and dried into cakes. She also showed them how to use Rocky Mountain juniper to make tea for colds and

© Macmillan/McGraw-Hill

GO ON

Page 2

fevers. Without her help, the explorers would not have known which plants were edible and healthful for them and which plants were poisonous.

4   The chokecherry was one of the most important plants to the tribes of Montana. The explorers found the chokecherry along their route. The seeds are poisonous if eaten raw, but the Native Americans knew how to remove the poisons. They dried the chokecherries, pounded them, and then formed them into cakes. Then they let them dry in the sun. Chokecherry cakes were a nutritious food for the explorers on the Lewis and Clark expedition. They ate them with soups and stew. They also made tea from the leaves.

5   Sacagawea knew that chokecherry tea helped cure stomach problems. She used the bark of the chokecherry tree to treat colds and coughs. After she removed the bark from the tree, she dried it. Then she boiled the dried bark to make tea. Modern scientists discovered that tea made from chokecherry bark could cure a sore throat. People who drank chokecherry tea healed from illnesses quickly.

6   The information Sacagawea passed on to the explorers helped many people survive serious diseases. This knowledge transferred from generation to generation. Today, chokecherry bark is used to flavor cough syrups. In fact, many modern medicines have their basis in natural remedies. By studying plants and biology, scientists have been able to create amazing medicines to keep people healthy.

1 Why is the order of the events in paragraph 1 important?

   A It shows Lewis and Clark as explorers.

   B It tells how Lewis met Clark.

   C It tells when Lewis and Clark met Sacagawea.

   D It shows how the explorers found the Missouri River.

2 After Lewis and Clark crossed the Rocky Mountains, they reached —

   F the Dakotas

   G the Pacific Ocean

   H St. Louis

   J Montana

© Macmillan/McGraw-Hill

Page 3

GO ON

3 What did Native Americans do before they added chokecherries to their food?

A They tasted the seeds.

B They boiled the bark.

C They cooked the cherries.

D They removed the poisons.

5 In paragraph 1, what does the word scoured mean?

A Explored

B Researched

C Cleaned

D Scrubbed

4 The reader can conclude that Sacagawea helped the explorers mainly by —

F teaching them how to use plants as food and medicine

G guiding them through the rivers and mountains

H giving them knowledge about modern medicine

J planting Rocky Mountain junipers to cure colds

6 Which word means about the same as specimens in paragraph 2?

F Plants

G Medicines

H Goals

J Samples

© Macmillan/McGraw-Hill

Page 4

GO ON

7 Which word has the same Greek root as the word <u>biology</u> in paragraph 6?

   A Bilingual

   B Biyearly

   C Biologist

   D Bicycle

8 Which word has the same Latin affix as the word <u>transferred</u> in paragraph 6?

   F Trails

   G Trampoline

   H Trains

   J Transport

9 How did Sacagawea transform the chokecherry tree into a healing tea? Explain your answer and support it with details from the article.

_____

_____

_____

_____

_____

_____

_____

Page 5

GO ON ▶

DIRECTIONS

Read the introduction and the passage that follows. Then read each question and fill in the correct answer on your answer document.

Esteban wrote this story about a boy named Ricardo. He wants you to review his story. As you read, think about the corrections and improvements that Esteban should make. Then answer the questions that follow.

Surfing Trip

(1) Ricardo opened his eyes, stretched, and looked out the window. (2) The day appeared sunny and clear. (3) Ricardo suddenly had an urge to grab his board to ride the waves for the day. (4) He packed his car and headed north on the Highway. (5) Eventually, he arrived at white horse beach. (6) He saw many other people wanted to surf that day as well—the place was packed! (7) Ricardo didn't want to daudle. (8) He ran toward the water, admiring the large swells. (9) He noticed his friend, Pierre, was already riding a huge wave. (10) Seeing no reason to be cawtious, Ricardo paddled out toward his friend to catch the next big swell.

Page 6

GO ON ➤

10 What change, if any, should be made in sentence 4?

    F Change *his* to **my**

    G Change *headed* to **heading**

    H Change *Highway* to **highway**

    J Make no change

11 What change, if any, should be made in sentence 5?

    A Change *he* to **him**

    B Insert a comma after *arrived*

    C Change *white horse beach* to **White Horse Beach**

    D Make no change

12 What change, if any, should be made in sentence 7?

    F Change *didn't* to **did'nt**

    G Change *daudle* to **dawdle**

    H Change the period to a question mark

    J Make no change

13 What change, if any, should be made in sentence 9?

    A Change *his* to **her**

    B Change *Pierre* to **pierre**

    C Change *riding* to **ride**

    D Make no change

14 What change, if any, should be made in sentence 10?

    F Change *Seeing* to **Seen**

    G Change *cawtious* to **cautious**

    H Change *paddled* to **paddling**

    J Make no change

BE SURE YOU HAVE RECORDED ALL OF YOUR ANSWERS ON THE ANSWER DOCUMENT.

Student Name _____

Grade 5 • Unit 2 • Week 1
Student Evaluation Chart

Tested Skills	Number Correct	Percent Correct
Reading Comprehension: *Sequence*, 1, 2, 3; *Draw Conclusions*, 4	/4	%
Short Answer: *Sequence*, 9	/3	%
Vocabulary Strategies: *Context Clues*, 5; *Synonyms*, 6; *Word Parts: Greek and Latin Roots/Affixes*, 7, 8	/4	%
Spelling: *Words with the Variant Vowel /ô/*, 12, 14	/2	%
Grammar, Mechanics, and Usage: *Common and Proper Nouns*, 10, 13; *Capitalize Proper Nouns*, 11	/3	%
Total Weekly Test Score	/16	%

Student Name _____

Date _____

Weekly Assessment

TESTED SKILLS AND STRATEGIES

- **Reading Comprehension**
- **Vocabulary Strategies**
- **Spelling**
- **Grammar, Mechanics, and Usage**

Macmillan/McGraw-Hill

Super Snakes

1   Many people fear snakes because they know only the common myths about these reptiles. Few snakes are deadly. However, poisonous <u>species</u> have certainly given snakes a bad reputation! Here are some facts about snakes that will help you better understand these members of the animal kingdom.

2   Snakes can survive in many <u>surroundings</u>, except for the polar regions of the world. Nature has given this creature many gifts. One of these gifts is the way its skin looks. Its patterns and coloring help the reptile hide from predators that will attack and eat it. Many snake species have skin the dull color of earth. The kinds that slither up trees may be bright green, like leaves.

3   Snakes can go for weeks or even months between meals, and some snakes eat only once or twice a year. Because of this, they do not need to hunt constantly for food.

4   The snake's lunging and flickering tongue may look frightening as it vibrates. But the tongue is part of an important sense organ for the snake. There is a special organ on the roof of its mouth. The snake uses it to smell prey and to find a mate. Some snakes, like the python, have special cells on top of their heads. These cells help them locate warm-blooded animals.

GO ON

Snakes use the muscles along the sides of their bodies to slither from place to place.

5   Most snakes feed on small mammals, such as rats and mice. Big snakes, like pythons, will attack much larger <u>prey</u>. <u>Alert</u> and watchful, the snake will often win what look like impossible battles.

6   The snake slithers on its belly because it has no legs. To move, it tightens and then relaxes the muscles along the sides of its body. It also can use its tail to push off against rocks or other objects. Because it can move so rapidly and quietly, the snake is a very effective hunter.

7   It is true that some snakes are poisonous. They use their poison to stun their prey before eating it. It is always best to be careful around snakes. Only an expert can tell which snakes are harmless and which are dangerous. However, a person can be careful around snakes without having a fear of them. The best advice is to find out if any poisonous snakes live in your area. In addition, if you are going camping or hiking, check beforehand to find out if the area is a habitat for poisonous snakes. If any poisonous snakes are found where you live or will be visiting, learn to identify them. Also learn what steps to take when you come across a poisonous snake. With knowledge like this, you can replace your fear with caution.

---

1 Which detail supports the idea that the snake is a very good hunter?

  A It moves very quietly.

  B It slithers along on its belly.

  C It can go for weeks without meals.

  D It feeds on small mammals.

2 In paragraph 1, the word <u>species</u> means —

  F kinds

  G babies

  H patterns

  J members

Page 3

GO ON

3 Look at the chart of information from the article.

Main Idea	Details
People should be cautious around snakes.	Check to see if poisonous snakes live in your area.
	Learn what to do if you run into a poisonous snake.

Which of the following belongs in the empty box?

A Run away if you see a poisonous snake.

B Learn to identify poisonous snakes.

C Tell your family members if you find a poisonous snake.

D Check to see if the poisonous snake has already eaten a meal.

4 What is the main idea of paragraph 2?

F Snakes cannot live in the polar regions of the world.

G Many snake species are the color of earth.

H Snakes have features that allow them to live in many places.

J A snake has nice patterns and coloring.

5 What is paragraph 4 mostly about?

A How the snake finds a mate

B Using the nose to smell things

C Looking for warm-blooded animals

D The snake's sense organs

© Macmillan/McGraw-Hill

GO ON

Page 4

6 In paragraph 2, what does the word <u>surroundings</u> mean?

    F Houses

    G Planets

    H Areas

    J Spaces

7 In paragraph 5, the word <u>alert</u> means —

    A safe

    B quick

    C aware

    D dangerous

8 What does the word <u>prey</u> mean in paragraph 5?

    F An animal hunted by another

    G A person who studies snakes

    H An environment or place to live

    J A snake that lives in trees

9 How does a snake use its body to help it survive? Explain your answer and support it with details from the article.

_____

_____

_____

_____

_____

_____

GO ON

DIRECTIONS

Read the introduction and the passage that follows. Then read each question and fill in the correct answer on your answer document.

Karla wrote a letter to her cousin. She wants you to review her letter. As you read, think about the corrections and improvements that Karla should make. Then answer the questions that follow.

(1) Dear Jessica,

(2) I got your letter, and I know you are nervous about moving to a new place. (3) I can give you some advice because my mom and dad are in the Navy so we move around a lot. (4) I have lived in four different countrys during my life. (5) It is exciting to meet people from around the world. (6) Some people I've met had different beliefes, but we still became friends. (7) Sometimes it might seem scary to go to a new schools, but school in every place I have lived is mostly the same. (8) There is always a lot of homework! (9) You will have many adventures and make new friend. (10) I hope you like your new home!

(11) your cousin,

(12) Kayla

© Macmillan/McGraw-Hill

10 What change, if any, should be made in sentence 4?

    F Change *four* to **for**

    G Change *countrys* to **countries**

    H Change *my* to **me**

    J Make no change

11 What change, if any, should be made in sentence 6?

    A Change *I've* to **I'll**

    B Change *met* to **meet**

    C Change *beliefes* to **beliefs**

    D Make no change

12 What change, if any, should be made in sentence 7?

    F Change *might* to **mite**

    G Change *schools* to **school**

    H Change *I* to **me**

    J Make no change

13 What change, if any, should be made in sentence 9?

    A Change *You will* to **You're**

    B Change *have* to **has**

    C Change *friend* to **friends**

    D Make no change

14 What is the **BEST** way to rewrite line 11?

    F your Cousin,

    G Your Cousin,

    H your cousin.

    J Your cousin,

BE SURE YOU HAVE RECORDED ALL OF YOUR ANSWERS ON THE ANSWER DOCUMENT.

Grade 5 • Unit 2 • Week 2
Student Evaluation Chart

Tested Skills	Number Correct	Percent Correct
Reading Comprehension: *Main Idea and Details*, 1, 3, 4, 5	/4	%
Short Answer: *Main Idea and Details*, 9	/3	%
Vocabulary Strategies: *Context Clues*, 2, 6, 7, 8	/4	%
Spelling: *Plurals*, 10, 11	/2	%
Grammar, Mechanics, and Usage: *Singular and Plural Nouns*, 12, 13; *Capitalization and Abbreviations in Letters*, 14	/3	%
Total Weekly Test Score	/16	%

Student Name _____

Date _____

Weekly Assessment

TESTED SKILLS AND STRATEGIES

- **Reading Comprehension**
- **Vocabulary Strategies**
- **Spelling**
- **Grammar, Mechanics, and Usage**

Macmillan/McGraw-Hill

Bug Robots

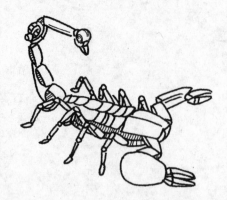
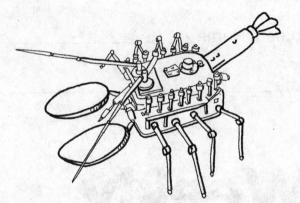

1   Investigating the world takes scientists to amazing places. They take rockets into space to explore the moon and planets. They travel deep beneath the ocean to explore the sea floor. Many places scientists want to investigate are dangerous for them to explore or impossible for them to reach, however. To solve this problem, they use robots built like insects. Scientists observe insects so they can learn how the insects move. Then they make robots that move as quickly and easily as bugs do.

2   Scientists make bug robots that have many legs, such as crickets, centipedes, cockroaches, and spiders. The bugs' legs are connected by joints, which allow them to bend in different directions. Some scientists who study bugs set up labs that are like gyms. There, the bugs can move, or exercise, in different ways.

3   One lab has a treadmill for centipedes and cockroaches, for example. As the bugs run on the treadmill, scientists take pictures of them using special cameras. Those cameras can capture thousands of images in seconds. By viewing these images, scientists can gain insight on how insects move their legs. Then they build robots with legs that move in the same way.

4   The bug robots have computers for brains, and scientists can program those computers to tell the robots' legs how to move. Then, when they

© Macmillan/McGraw-Hill

GO ON

Page 2

release the robots onto the field, they make them move using remote controls. Some scientists are trying to make a robot with legs that can be removed and replaced with different ones. This would allow the robot to move just as easily in small spaces as in large ones.

5   Bug robots have been used in a number of investigations. They have traveled on rockets to Mars, crawled over Martian soil, and squeezed between Martian rocks. As scientists improve bug robots, they will become even more important. They may be able to crawl into tiny places on the space station and make repairs. They may be able to withstand the heat of volcanoes. They may also be able to climb through dangerous areas on Earth and rescue people who are trapped or hurt. Bug robots will help scientists make new discoveries and conquer problems they have been struggling with.

6   One thing to remember about bug robots is that they are really tiny computers. As they continue to improve, they will do more important things. It is especially important to put tiny cameras in the robots. That way, when a robot walks on Mars, it can take pictures that scientists could never see otherwise.

© Macmillan/McGraw-Hill

1 Based on the information in this article, why do scientists study insects?

   A To learn how they move

   B To understand how to control them

   C To use them to rescue people

   D To find them new places to live

2 The author mentions the planet Mars because —

   F bug robots have gone there

   G scientists know little about it

   H people would like to visit it

   J scientists are building bug robots there

3 Paragraph 4 was written mainly to explain —

   A how bug robots move

   B how scientists build remote controls

   C where bug robots will go in the future

   D why scientists use computers

4 The author's purpose in paragraph 5 is to —

   F convince other scientists to use bug robots

   G show how bug robots may be used in the future

   H explain why insects need to be studied further

   J teach people what to do in dangerous situations

5 In paragraph 1, the word investigating means —

   A studying

   B helping

   C finding

   D understanding

6 In paragraph 1, the word observe means the same as —

   F trap

   G purchase

   H value

   J watch

© Macmillan/McGraw-Hill

GO ON

Page 4

7 What does the word <u>insight</u> mean in paragraph 3?

   A Satisfaction

   B Awareness

   C Interest

   D Advice

8 In paragraph 5, the word <u>conquer</u> comes from a Latin root that means —

   F discuss

   G send

   H quiet

   J defeat

9 What is the author's purpose for writing this article? Explain your answer and support it with details from the article.

_____

_____

_____

_____

_____

_____

_____

Page 5

GO ON ▶

DIRECTIONS

Read the introduction and the passage that follows. Then read each question and fill in the correct answer on your answer document.

Leslie wrote this story in her journal. She wants you to review her work. As you read, think about the corrections and improvements that Leslie should make. Then answer the questions that follow.

My Big Brother

(1) My older brother a college student came home last week for the summer. (2) Now he's looking for a summer job. (3) He has applyed for three different jobs. (4) I bet he'll be offered all three of them because he is very qualified. (5) The job he wants the most is at "Camp Sunshine" as a counselor. (6) He really enjoys working with childs. (7) After he gets a job, he says he'll take me to an amusement park one weekend because I love riding roller coaster.

GO ON

10 What is the **BEST** way to rewrite sentence 1?

   F My older brother a college student, came home last week for the summer.

   G My older, brother a college student came home last week for the summer.

   H My older brother, a college student, came home last week for the summer.

   J My older brother, a college student came home last week for the summer.

11 What change, if any, should be made in sentence 3?

   A Change *applyed* to applied

   B Change *jobs* to job

   C Change the period to a question mark

   D Make no change

12 What change, if any, should be made in sentence 4?

   F Change *he'll* to he'd

   G Change *them* to it

   H Change *qualified* to qualifyed

   J Make no change

13 What change, if any, should be made in sentence 6?

   A Change *enjoys* to enjoyes

   B Change *working* to worked

   C Change *childs* to children

   D Make no change

14 What change, if any, should be made in sentence 7?

   F Change *he'll* to he all

   G Change *riding* to ride

   H Change *roller coaster* to roller coasters

   J Make no change

BE SURE YOU HAVE RECORDED ALL OF YOUR ANSWERS
ON THE ANSWER DOCUMENT.

Grade 5 • Unit 2 • Week 3
Student Evaluation Chart

Tested Skills	Number Correct	Percent Correct
Reading Comprehension: *Main Idea and Details*, 1; *Author's Purpose*, 2, 3, 4	/4	%
Short Answer: *Author's Purpose*, 9	/3	%
Vocabulary Strategies: *Context Clues*, 5, 6, 7; *Greek and Latin Roots*, 8	/4	%
Spelling: *Words with Inflectional Endings*, 11, 12	/2	%
Grammar, Mechanics, and Usage: *Appositives*, 10; *Plural Forms*, 13; *More Plural Nouns*, 14	/3	%
Total Weekly Test Score	/16	%

Student Name _____

Date _____

Weekly Assessment

TESTED SKILLS AND STRATEGIES

- **Reading Comprehension**
- **Vocabulary Strategies**
- **Spelling**
- **Grammar, Mechanics, and Usage**

Mc Graw Hill **Macmillan/McGraw-Hill**

Up, Up, and Away!

1   More than a century before the Wright brothers' famous plane flight, a different type of object rose into the sky. It was a balloon filled with heated air. The year was 1783, and the place was France. Two brothers named Montgolfier launched the very first hot-air balloon. It was made of four huge pieces of fabric and paper, held together by almost 2,000 buttons. The balloon stayed in the air about ten minutes. There were no passengers because that would have been too dangerous. Instead the balloon carried a sheep, a duck, and a rooster.

2   After this historic event, interest in balloons grew quickly. Inventors began competing to see who could make the safest balloon and take the longest flight. Some people continued to work on balloons filled with heated air. Others developed balloons filled with hydrogen gas, which is lighter than air.

3   A few months after the flight of the Montgolfier balloon, another first in balloon history took place. A Frenchman named Jacques Charles launched a beautiful balloon made of silk. It was filled with hydrogen gas. Charles's balloon looked lovely as it floated through the air.

4   In November of that same year, the Montgolfier brothers again made history. A giant balloon they had constructed carried humans into the air

© Macmillan/McGraw-Hill

Page 2

GO ON ▶

for the first time. One of the passengers was a French science teacher who had helped with the Montgolfier flight of the animals. His companion was a French nobleman. The two men sailed over Paris for 25 minutes. The hot air produced by a fire of burning straw was used to <u>inflate</u> the giant balloon. It was a wonderful flight until the balloon caught on fire. Luckily, no one was hurt.

5   The first balloon flight in the United States traveled from Philadelphia, Pennsylvania, to New Jersey in 1793. George Washington was one of the spectators. He watched as the <u>anchored</u> balloon was released so that it could soar into the air. Balloons had officially entered into United States history.

6   While the first hot-air balloons were used for adventure, people soon saw that they could be used for military purposes, such as delivering messages across long distances. During World War II, they served another purpose. Wires were strung between balloons, forming a trap that military planners hoped would stop enemy airplanes.

7   More recently, balloons have been used to travel long distances. In 1978, a balloon called the *Double Eagle* crossed the Atlantic Ocean. The balloon was filled with helium and carried three passengers. In 1991, a hot-air balloon crossed the Pacific Ocean. Later that year, two men completed a balloon flight around the world. It was a thrilling feat.

8   Today, many hot-air balloons are used for science and studying the weather. So, while hot-air balloons often are used for fun, they still are used for serious purposes as well.

1 In paragraph 1, <u>launched</u> means —

  A watched

  B sent forth

  C bought

  D read about

2 In paragraph 5, <u>anchored</u> means —

  F secured to the ground

  G released into the air

  H filled with passengers

  J equipped with safety nets

Page 3

GO ON

3 Read the diagram below to answer the following question.

Fact		Opinion	
Others developed balloons filled with hydrogen gas, which is lighter than air.	Today meteorological balloons carry scientific tools, such as barometers, that measure the air pressure, wind speed, and ozone levels.	It was a wonderful flight until the balloon caught on fire.	

Which statement belongs in the empty box?

A *The balloon stayed in the air about ten minutes.*

B *Charles's balloon looked lovely as it floated through the air.*

C *The two men sailed over Paris for 25 minutes.*

D *Some people continued to work on balloons filled with heated air.*

---

4 The first hot-air balloon flight took place in —

F 1783

G 1785

H 1978

J 1991

5 In paragraph 7, which words indicate that the author is stating his opinion?

A *More recently*

B *the* Double Eagle

C *thrilling feat*

D *around the world*

© Macmillan/McGraw-Hill

GO ON ➡

6 In paragraph 2, the word hydrogen comes from a Greek root that means —

   F light

   G safe

   H across

   J water

7 In paragraph 4, what does the word inflate mean?

   A Change the motion of

   B Take apart

   C Expand with air

   D Create

8 What fact supports the idea that 1793 was an important year in hot-air balloon history?

   F The first hot-air balloon flight in the United States occurred.

   G A sheep, duck, and a rooster flew in a hot-air balloon.

   H Hydrogen was used inside a hot-air balloon.

   J A hot-air balloon delivered a message during World War II.

9 Which facts does the author use to explain that hot-air balloons can be used for purposes other than adventure? Explain your answer and support it with details from the article.

_____

_____

_____

_____

_____

Page 5

GO ON ▶

DIRECTIONS

Read the introduction and the passage that follows. Then read each question and fill in the correct answer on your answer document.

Vicky wrote this report for science. She wants you to review her paper. As you read, think about the corrections and improvements that Vicky should make. Then answer the questions that follow.

Sir George Cayley

(1) Many people tried to invent flying machines during the 1700s and 1800s. (2) An Englishman named Sir George Cayley realized that studying how bird's fly was an important part of creating a flying machine. (3) In the past, one inventor had designed his flying machine's wings to flap like a bird's wing. (4) Cayley watched birds soar in the air. (5) He realized that wings should'nt flap, and they should be shaped so as to create lift. (6) Cayley designed the first glider that was able to carry humans. (7) A ten-year-old boy was the first person in history to fly when he made a short flight in Cayleys glider. (8)Tha'ts why some people call him the "Father of Aviation."

© Macmillan/McGraw-Hill

GO ON

10 What change, if any, should be made in sentence 2?

   F Change *Englishman* to englishman

   G Change *bird's* to birds

   H Change *creating* to create

   J Make no change

11 What change, if any, should be made in sentence 3?

   A Change *others* to other's

   B Change *machine's* to machines

   C Change *flap* to flaps

   D Make no change

12 What change, if any, should be made in sentence 5?

   F Change *they* to them

   G Change *should'nt* to shouldn't

   H Change *shaped* to shaping

   J Make no change

13 What change, if any, should be made in sentence 7?

   A Change *was* to were

   B Change *fly* to flying

   C Change *Cayleys* to Cayley's

   D Make no change

14 What change, if any, should be made in sentence 8?

   F Change *Tha'ts* to That's

   G Change *some* to sum

   H Change *him* to he

   J Make no change

BE SURE YOU HAVE RECORDED ALL OF YOUR ANSWERS ON THE ANSWER DOCUMENT.

Grade 5 • Unit 2 • Week 4
Student Evaluation Chart

Tested Skills	Number Correct	Percent Correct
Reading Comprehension: *Fact and Opinion, 3, 4, 5, 8*	/4	%
Short Answer: *Fact and Opinion, 9*	/3	%
Vocabulary Strategies: *Context Clues, 1, 2; Greek Roots, 6; Context Clues, 7*	/4	%
Spelling: *Contractions, 12, 14*	/2	%
Grammar, Mechanics, and Usage: *Adding s or 's,10, 11; Possessive Nouns, 13*	/3	%
Total Weekly Test Score	/16	%

Student Name _____

Date _____

Weekly Assessment

TESTED SKILLS AND STRATEGIES

- **Reading Comprehension**
- **Vocabulary Strategies**
- **Spelling**
- **Grammar, Mechanics, and Usage**

The Life of a Hurricane

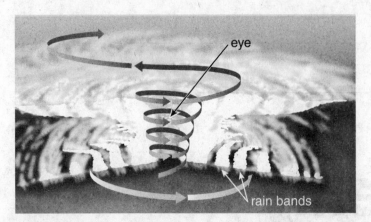

eye

rain bands

Usually the weather is calm in the eye of the hurricane, which may range from 2 miles to 200 miles in diameter. Rain bands spiral toward the center of the hurricane, often bringing high winds and heavy rainfall; calmer weather is found between the rain bands.

1   What do hurricanes, cyclones, and typhoons have in common? They are all different names for the same severe tropical storm that is known as a *tropical cyclone*. In this article, the word *hurricane* will be used to discuss this type of storm.

2   What causes a hurricane to develop over ocean water? At least three elements must be present. First, the water must be warm enough to give off heat and moisture into the <u>atmosphere</u>. Second, evaporated water already available in the air must mix with the heat and moisture rising from the ocean. Finally, easterly winds must be present. The wind moves the heat and evaporated water high into the atmosphere. Then Earth's rotation begins to work against the easterly winds. This twists the growing storm into a cylinder. The center of this cylinder is called the *eye*.

3   When the heat and moisture from the ocean's surface come into <u>contact</u> with the cooler air higher up, thunderstorms develop. Then the cooler air travels back toward the ocean's surface and pulls more moisture from the ocean. Once that moisture rises into the thunderclouds, it is released as torrential rain. This type of rain usually accompanies hurricanes. The

© Macmillan/McGraw-Hill

GO ON

Page 2

winds increase in speed and begin to move the enormous storm across the ocean. As long as hurricanes remain over water, they can keep increasing in size and strength.

4   What causes the storm to end? Sometimes a hurricane dies when it travels into the path of strong westerly winds. This disturbs its course and may cause the storm to travel over cooler northern waters. Without the energy from the evaporated ocean water, the storm finally loses power and dies out.

5   At other times, a hurricane travels until it hits land. Once it is over land, it causes enormous damage. Tornadoes may form in the rain bands. High winds knock over structures. The ocean surge floods towns and also causes extensive destruction of property. But without the warm ocean water as an energy source, a hurricane over land also loses power. Eventually, it ends up as rain showers.

1 What does the caption under the first diagram describe?

   A The parts of a hurricane

   B The causes of a hurricane

   C The steps in a hurricane's development

   D The elements that must be present for a hurricane to form

2 In paragraph 2, the author describes —

   F how Earth rotates in space

   G the reason hurricanes have three different names

   H why winds sometimes become stronger

   J the three elements needed to create a hurricane

Page 3

3 What happens just after heat and moisture from the ocean's surface mix with cooler air?

A The hurricane dies out.

B Thunderstorms develop.

C The storm moves across the ocean.

D A cylinder shape takes form.

4 The author describes hurricanes as —

F fierce storms

G exciting to watch

H helpful for growing crops

J types of tornadoes

5 In paragraph 2, what does the word <u>atmosphere</u> mean?

A Air around the earth

B Land near the sea

C A storm over the ocean

D A large area of ocean

6 Which meaning of the word <u>contact</u> best fits the way it is used in paragraph 3?

F An observation

G The act or state of touching

H To be in communication

J To form a relationship

GO ON ➜

7 In paragraph 5, what does the word destruction mean?

   A Storm

   B Injuries

   C Damage

   D Flooding

8 Which meaning best fits the word property in paragraph 5?

   F A written piece of work

   G A person under a contract

   H A piece of land or a possession

   J A quality or a characteristic

9 How does a hurricane form? Explain your answer and support it with details from the article.

_____

_____

_____

_____

_____

_____

GO ON ▶

DIRECTIONS

Read the introduction and the passage that follows. Then read each question and fill in the correct answer on your answer document.

Jessica wrote this story in her journal. She wants you to review her work. As you read, think about the corrections and improvements that Jessica should make. Then answer the questions that follow.

A New Pet

(1) This weekend my family adopted a dog. (2) We got her from a shelter that rescues dog's and cat's. (3) The people at the shelter were very helpful. (4) They suggested we get the book Understanding Your Dog to help us learn how to care for our new pet. (5) My parents asked me to give our new dog a name, so I named her Lily. (6) Lily does not know how to sit or play fetch yet. (7) She likes to galop around our backyard and jump on my little brother. (8) We may bring her to the kennel so she can learn how to behave. (9) They have class's for dogs and their new owners.

GO ON ➡

Page 6

10 What change, if any, should be made in sentence 2?

   F Change *We* to Us

   G Change *rescues* to **rescue**

   H Change *dog's and cat's* to **dogs and cats**

   J Make no change

11 What change, if any, should be made in sentence 4?

   A Change *suggested* to **suggests**

   B Underline *Understanding Your Dog*

   C Change *new* to **knew**

   D Make no change

12 What change, if any, should be made in sentence 7?

   F Change *likes* to **like**

   G Change *galop* to **gallop**

   H Insert a comma after *backyard*

   J Make no change

13 What change, if any, should be made in sentence 8?

   A Change *bring* to **brings**

   B Change *kennel* to **kenel**

   C Change *behave* to **behaved**

   D Make no change

14 What change, if any, should be made in sentence 9?

   F Change *class's* to **classes**

   G Insert a comma before *and*

   H Change *their* to **there**

   J Make no change

BE SURE YOU HAVE RECORDED ALL OF YOUR ANSWERS ON THE ANSWER DOCUMENT.

Page 7

Grade 5 • Unit 2 • Week 5
Student Evaluation Chart

Tested Skills	Number Correct	Percent Correct
Reading Comprehension: Description, 1, 2, 4; Sequence, 3	/4	%
Short Answer: Description, 9	/3	%
Vocabulary Strategies: Context Clues, 5, 7; Multiple-Meaning Words, 6, 8	/4	%
Spelling: Closed Syllables, 12, 13	/2	%
Grammar, Mechanics, and Usage: Plurals and Possessives, 10, 14; Punctuating Titles, 11	/3	%
Total Weekly Test Score	/16	%

Student Name _____

Date _____

Weekly Assessment

TESTED SKILLS AND STRATEGIES

- **Reading Comprehension**
- **Vocabulary Strategies**
- **Spelling**
- **Grammar, Mechanics, and Usage**

Mc Graw Hill Macmillan/McGraw-Hill

Raven the Trickster and Fish Hawk:
A Retelling of a Native American Tale

1   Tricksters have ways of getting what they want. However, they often get themselves in trouble. Raven was a trickster who got in trouble quite frequently. One day, a bird named Fish Hawk was <u>unfortunate</u> enough to meet Raven on the riverbank. Raven acted very kindly toward Fish Hawk, hoping the bird would do him a favor.

2   "Ah, my dearest friend," Raven greeted Fish Hawk. "The weather has turned cold and bitter. Let us go to your house and warm ourselves."

3   Fish Hawk was too polite to refuse. But it was without enthusiasm that he led Raven to his home. Once inside, Raven glanced about slyly and noticed that the hawk had laid in a large supply of food. Fish Hawk also had made his home quite comfortable with drinking gourds and soft blankets of leaves and grasses.

4   "What a lot of <u>merchandise</u> you have here," sneaky Raven said. "You could open your own store and sell your wares!"

5   When Fish Hawk said nothing in response, Raven continued. "All the birds that have wasted the summer singing and flitting about, instead of storing food for the winter, would be eager to buy some of this. You will

GO ON

Page 2

need a treasurer to help you with sales and to help you collect profits on these goods. That requires a lot of time and effort! Why don't I visit with you during the winter months, and we can share some of the burdens of shopkeeping and housekeeping?"

6   Fish Hawk doubted the wisdom of this plan, but he let Raven stay with him. It soon became clear that Raven would not lift a feather to help his kind host. In time, Fish Hawk grew tired of his lazy guest. But Raven talked to him sweetly, saying, "Don't worry, dear friend. This beach will be covered with fish, and you will not have to catch them. I'll get our dinner for us while you rest."

7   Poor Fish Hawk decided to give Raven another chance. Yet weeks passed by and Raven did nothing to help. He made his host gather food for both of them while he slept and ate up the meals. Thanking Fish Hawk many times after each large dinner, he would say, "What a rich, wise friend you are! I have so much <u>appreciation</u> for your kindness. Words can hardly express my feelings." He would always conclude this speech by again assuring Fish Hawk that he would catch fish. But, of course, nothing came of this empty promise.

8   Fish Hawk finally grew disgusted by Raven's laziness and greed, and he flew away from his own house. "That will teach you, Raven!" he called out. "Now you will have to fend for yourself!" He hoped to <u>educate</u> Raven by teaching him a lesson. Yet deep in his heart, he knew that the old trickster would never change.

9   Fish Hawk soon built himself a cozy new home. And Raven had to find his own dinner from then on.

Page 3

1 What is one theme of this story?

   A Some people will never change.

   B Be loyal to your friends.

   C It is easy to get what you want.

   D It is important to be kind to guests.

2 Why is the phrase, "Raven glanced about slyly" important to the story?

   F It shows that Raven has keen eyesight.

   G It suggests that Raven is very polite.

   H It shows that Raven admires Fish Hawk's house.

   J It suggests that Raven plans to trick Fish Hawk.

3 When Raven thanks Fish Hawk many times, it shows that Raven is —

   A very grateful

   B a hard worker

   C planning on helping out

   D skilled at tricking others

4 What is one lesson the reader may learn from this story?

   F Hard work and persistence will almost always pay off in the end.

   G If you take advantage of others, you may find yourself alone.

   H Birds can never be trusted.

   J It is better to be honest from the beginning, than to bury yourself in lies.

5 Greed is to kindness as unfortunate is to —

   A lucky

   B kindly

   C silly

   D unhappy

6 Gather is to collect as merchandise is to —

   F prices

   G goods

   H animals

   J shoppers

GO ON

7 Which words in paragraph 7 help the reader understand the meaning of <u>appreciation</u>?

   A *another chance*

   B *for both of them*

   C *Thanking Fish Hawk*

   D *a rich, wise friend*

8 In paragraph 8, which word means about the same as <u>educate</u>?

   F *fend*

   G *teach*

   H *called*

   J *change*

9 Why does Fish Hawk leave his own home at the end of the story? Explain your answer and support it with details from the story.

_____

_____

_____

_____

_____

_____

Page 5

DIRECTIONS

Read the introduction and the passage that follows. Then read each question and fill in the correct answer on your answer document.

Max wrote this movie review. He wants you to review his work. As you read, think about the corrections and improvements that Max should make. Then answer the questions that follow.

A Very Funny Movie

(1) Would you like to see a really funny movie? (2) Then I advise you to go see *The Tale of a Dog's Tail.* (3) It is the funniest movie I've seen in resent weeks. (4) The movie are about two sisters and their dog, Poochie. (5) Something mysterious causes Poochie's tail to keep growing and growing. (6) His unusual tail create all kinds of problems! (7) You're going to love the humor in this movie, and you'll be happy you listened to my advice.

10 What change, if any, should be made in sentence 3?

    F Change *funniest* to **funnier**

    G Change *I've* to **I'ave**

    H Change *resent* to **recent**

    J Make no change

11 What is the **BEST** way to rewrite sentence 4?

    A The movie is about two sister and their dog, Poochie.

    B The movie is about two sisters and their dog, Poochie.

    C The movie were about two sisters and their dog, Poochie.

    D The movie being about two sisters and their dog, Poochie.

12 Which word in sentence 5 is an action verb?

    F *something*

    G *mysterious*

    H *causes*

    J *tail*

13 What is the **BEST** way to rewrite sentence 6?

    A His unusual tail creates all kinds of problems!

    B His unusual tail creating all kinds of problems!

    C His unusual tail creates all kind of problem!

    D His unusual tail is creating all kinds of problem!

14 What change, if any, should be made in sentence 7?

    F Change *going* to **gone**

    G Change *humor* to **humer**

    H Change *listened* to **listens**

    J Make no change

BE SURE YOU HAVE RECORDED ALL OF YOUR ANSWERS ON THE ANSWER DOCUMENT.

Grade 5 • Unit 3 • Week 1
Student Evaluation Chart

Tested Skills	Number Correct	Percent Correct
Reading Comprehension: *Theme, 1, 4; Plot, 2; Character, 3*	/4	%
Short Answer: *Theme, 9*	/3	%
Vocabulary Strategies: *Analogies: 5, 6; Context Clues, 7;* *Synonyms, 8*	/4	%
Spelling: *Words with Open Syllables;* 10, 14	/2	%
Grammar, Mechanics, and **Usage:** *Subject-Verb Agreement,* 11, 13 ; *Action Verbs, 12*	/3	%
Total Weekly Test Score	/16	%

Student Name _____

Date _____

Weekly Assessment

TESTED SKILLS AND STRATEGIES

- **Reading Comprehension**
- **Vocabulary Strategies**
- **Spelling**
- **Grammar, Mechanics, and Usage**

Mc Graw Hill **Macmillan/McGraw-Hill**

Read this selection. Then answer the questions that follow it.

Hans in Luck: A Retelling of a Tale
from *The Young Folks Treasury*

1   After seven years of hard work, Hans asked his master for his wages. The master gave Hans a big piece of gold. The young man took off for his village, anxious to see his mother after such a long absence. On the road, Hans met a man on a fine horse. The youth said, "How fortunate you are to be riding, while I weary myself trudging along."

2   The horseman <u>descended</u> from the animal and proposed a trade. "I'll trade you my stallion for that piece of gold in your hand."

3   When Hans agreed, the rider thrust the horse's bridle into the young man's hands. "Just utter 'C'ck! C'ck!' and the horse will gallop like lightning," he instructed and walked away.

Page 2

GO ON

Weekly Assessment

4   Of course, Hans immediately attempted to gallop. But the stallion instantly threw him off, and he landed in a ditch beside the road.

5   It was not long before a peasant woman happened to pass by, leading a cow. She was startled to see a young man in the ditch. Hans, rubbing a sore arm and leg, said to her, "I see you have a nice, quiet cow that no doubt gives refreshing milk. I'd rather your cow accompany me instead of this brute of a horse."

6   The peasant woman agreed to trade her cow for the horse. So Hans continued along the route to his village, driving the cow along and whistling merrily.

7   The day grew hot, and Hans grew thirsty. He tried to milk the cow. But he went about it in an awkward way, and the animal gave him a swift kick. Sweating, thirsty, and bruised, Hans was in great despair by this point.

8   Then along came a butcher driving a horse-drawn cart. In the cart was a huge pig. Hans told the butcher, "How I wish I had a pig. I'd have it butchered to make sausages and other delicacies."

9   "I'd be happy to trade you this prime pig for that worthless looking cow," offered the butcher. The deal was quickly completed.

10   Before twilight fell, Hans made even another trade: He swapped the pig for a goose. "My mother can use its soft feathers to stuff a pillow," he told himself.

11   Finally he entered his village. The first person he saw was a scissors-grinder at his trade. "Where did you get that goose?" the man asked Hans.

12   "I exchanged it for my pig," Hans replied, then worked backward to relate all his adventures to the scissors-grinder. The man suggested that Hans trade the goose for his grinding stone, and Hans consented.

13   But with each step Hans took, the stone seemed to grow heavier. Soon he laid it by the side of a stream that ran through the village. When he stooped to drink, the weighty stone tumbled into the water.

14   Free of any tiresome burdens now, Hans exclaimed, "I'm the luckiest man alive!" And he hastened homeward to his mother.

GO ON

Page 3

1 Look at this diagram of information from the story.

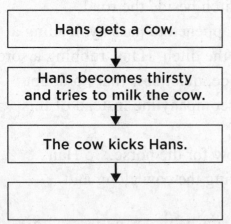

| Hans gets a cow. |
| Hans becomes thirsty and tries to milk the cow. |
| The cow kicks Hans. |
| |

Which of these belongs in the empty box?

A Hans goes home to see his mother.

B Hans trades the cow for a pig.

C Hans trades the cow for a goose.

D Hans enters the village.

2 On Hans's journey, which event happens first?

F Hans trades his cow for a pig.

G A man rides by on a fine horse.

H A horse flings Hans into a ditch.

J Hans swaps his pig for a goose.

3 What happens just before Hans meets the peasant woman?

A He tries to milk a cow.

B A cow kicks him.

C The horse throws him off.

D He meets a butcher.

4 What happens just after Hans gets a pig?

F He attempts to milk a cow.

G He asks his master for his salary.

H He swaps his gold for a horse.

J He trades the pig for a goose.

5 In paragraph 2, the word descended means —

A led to

B came down

C traded for

D jumped away

© Macmillan/McGraw-Hill

Page 4

GO ON ▶

6 Which word is pronounced the same as the word <u>route</u> in paragraph 6?

  F Rut

  G Root

  H Rote

  J Rot

7 Which word means almost the same as despair?

  A Liveliness

  B Joyfulness

  C Greediness

  D Hopelessness

8 In paragraph 12, what does <u>consented</u> mean?

  F Denied

  G Agreed

  H Wondered

  J Demanded

9 What happens after Hans trades the goose for the grinding stone? Explain your answer and support it with details from the story.

_____

_____

_____

_____

_____

Page 5

GO ON

© Macmillan/McGraw-Hill

DIRECTIONS

Read the introduction and the passage that follows. Then read each question and fill in the correct answer on your answer document.

Vito wrote this story about the school library. He wants you to review his story. As you read, think about the corrections and improvements that Vito should make. Then answer the questions that follow.

The Perfect Poem

(1) Last week, Marabel goes to the library to search for a book of poems. (2) She liked to meender along the rows of books, taking her time. (3) Finally she found the perfect poem about patriets in the American Revolution. (4) She picked it up and read it softly to herself.

(5)   But up from the wakening waters

(6)   Comes the cool, fresh. morning breeze,

(7)   lifting the banner of Britain,

(8)   And whispering to the trees

(9)   Of the swift gliding boats on the waters

(10)   That are nearing the fog-shrouded land,

(11)   With the old Green Mountain Lion,

(12)   And his daring patriot band.

GO ON ➡

Page 6

10 What change, if any, should be made in sentence 1?

   F Change *goes* to **went**

   G Change *search* to **searching**

   H Underline a *book of poems*

   J Make no change

11 What change, if any, should be made in sentence 2?

   A Change *liked* to **liking**

   B Change *meender* to **meander**

   C Change *taking* to **took**

   D Make no change

12 What change, if any, should be made in sentence 3?

   F Change *found* to **finding**

   G Change *American Revolution* to **american revolution**

   H Change *patriets* to **patriots**

   J Make no change

13 What change, if any, should be made in line 6 in the poem?

   A Change *Comes* to **Come**

   B Delete the comma after *cool*

   C Delete the period after *fresh*

   D Make no change

14 What change, if any, should be made in line 7 in the poem?

   F Change *lifting* to **Lifting**

   G Change *banner* to **baner**

   H Change *Britain* to **britain**

   J Make no change

Page 7

BE SURE YOU HAVE RECORDED ALL OF YOUR ANSWERS ON THE ANSWER DOCUMENT.

Student Name _____

Grade 5 • Unit 3 • Week 2
Student Evaluation Chart

Tested Skills	Number Correct	Percent Correct
Reading Comprehension: *Sequence*, 1, 2, 3, 4	/4	%
Short Answer: *Sequence*, 9	/3	%
Vocabulary Strategies: *Context Clues*, 5, 7, 8 ; *Homophones*, 6	/4	%
Spelling: *Words with Open Syllables (V/V)*, 11, 12	/2	%
Grammar, Mechanics, and Usage: *Verb Tenses*, 10; *Capitalization and Punctuation in Poetry*, 13, 14	/3	%
Total Weekly Test Score	/16	%

Student Name _____

Date _____

Weekly Assessment

TESTED SKILLS AND STRATEGIES

- **Reading Comprehension**
- **Vocabulary Strategies**
- **Spelling**
- **Grammar, Mechanics, and Usage**

Mc Graw Hill **Macmillan/McGraw-Hill**

What Are Ballads?

1   A ballad is a form of poetry. It is also a form of song. Ballads have been written in many countries across the globe. Many of the most popular ballads were written in Europe and the United States. Most English ballads date from the fifteenth century. Most American ballads date from the settlement of the West. Historians feel it is important to preserve ballads because they give us information about the past.

2   Ballads were written to be sung, but they are mostly stories. They tell of heroes who did important deeds and worked in clever ways. Like short stories, ballads have characters, settings, and themes. They focus on action and tell about events. Ballads sometimes reveal an important message.

3   Usually, ballads are about heroes, who may be real or make-believe. But whether or not an event actually happened, the story sent a message. Some of the most popular ballads from England are about a hero named Robin Hood. Robin Hood had clever ways of doing important deeds.

4   In one story, Robin Hood robbed from the rich to give to the poor. This sent an important message about sharing wealth and helping others.

GO ON

Page 2

The Robin Hood ballads are unique to England, but in many ways they are like ballads from other countries. At first, they were sung in public. Later, they were written down.

5   Corridos are a form of ballad specific to Mexico. They represent the ideas and concerns of the Mexican people. Like ballads from Europe and the United States, corridos have been around hundreds of years. They were written by people who had important ideas to share. They sang songs about real events. Often, the events were sad. They involved ordinary people who became heroes. At the time they were written, they explained how people felt about events that affected their lives. Corridos always follow a set pattern. The song begins with a reason, gives details about the event and the hero involved, and ends with a farewell to the hero.

6   Ballads are always sung, even though they are mostly stories. In the early years, people sang ballads at public gatherings. Like songs, ballads usually have a refrain. A refrain is a word, a phrase, or a line that is repeated after each stanza. Most ballads that have survived for hundreds of years have verses in four lines. Often, they rhyme. Sometimes, but not always, ballads are performed to music.

7   Sometimes, ballads are accompanied by dance. Still, the words are more important than the melody. One ballad can be sung to different melodies, for example. Ballads were created to tell stories because they express important ideas. They are a clever way of explaining the things people thought were important.

8   No one knows for sure whether ballads were written by one person or by many different people. People who study ballads argue about that. Probably, one author wrote a ballad, and then over time, other generations changed it. In this way, ballads are like other forms of folklore. The people, or the folk, make these tales fit certain events. The songs have similar themes, but the heroes and the stories are different. The words and phrases can change, but the message of the story is the same.

1 Ballads are different from songs because ballads —

   A are usually performed as dances

   B were written by one person

   C focus more on words than on melodies

   D have a refrain

2 How is Robin Hood similar to heroes in many other ballads?

   F He sent messages to people.

   G His actions made him a clever hero.

   H He was from England.

   J His stories were hard to believe.

3 Which element is similar across all ballads?

   A They tell stories of events.

   B They are sung in public places.

   C They are performed to music.

   D They include dance.

4 Why did the author write this article?

   F To instruct readers how to write a ballad

   G To inform readers about the history of ballads

   H To entertain readers with a ballad about Robin Hood

   J To convince readers that ballads are the most interesting form of poetry

5 In paragraph 1, the word <u>globe</u> means —

   A world

   B circle

   C people

   D image

6 Which definition of <u>preserve</u> best fits the way it is used in paragraph 1?

   F To keep from spoiling

   G To save or keep

   H A kind of fruit jam

   J An area set aside for animals

Page 4

7 In paragraph 2, the word <u>reveal</u> means —

A create

B tell

C understand

D change

8 In paragraph 8, what does the word <u>generations</u> mean?

F Things that are used in creating folklores

G Groups of people born at certain times

H Things that people make or generate

J Groups of people from certain countries

9 How are corridos similar to ballads from Europe and the United States? Explain your answer and support it with details from the article.

_____

_____

_____

_____

_____

_____

_____

Page 5

GO ON ➤

DIRECTIONS

Read the introduction and the passage that follows. Then read each question and fill in the correct answer on your answer document.

Juliet wrote this report. She wants you to review her work. As you read, think about the corrections and improvements that Juliet should make. Then answer the questions that follow.

César Chávez

(1) In the 1950s, César Chávez was an important person in California.

(2) At the time, he was working in an apricot orchard south of San Jose.

(3) Like Martin Luther King, Jr., César Chávez fought for equal rights.

(4) Martin Luther King, Jr., was born in the southrn state of Georgia and fought for the rights of African Americans. (5) César Chávez was born in Arizona and fought for the rights of Mexican Americans. (6) During the 1950s, many Mexican Americans were working on farms in California. (7) Chávez realized that the farm workers faced many problems. (8) They werent treated fairly by the farm owners. (9) Altho many people opposed his beliefs, Chávez worked hard to help farm workers get fair treatment and higher pay.

GO ON ➡

10 Which word in sentence 2 is a main verb?

    F *time*

    G *was*

    H *working*

    J *south*

11 What change, if any, should be made in sentence 4?

    A Change *southrn* to **southern**

    B Change *state* to **State**

    C Change *fought* to **fighted**

    D Make no change

12 Which word in sentence 6 is a helping verb?

    F *many*

    G *were*

    H *working*

    J *farms*

13 What change, if any, should be made in sentence 8?

    A Change *They* to **Them**

    B Change *werent* to **weren't**

    C Change *treated* to **treating**

    D Make no change

14 What change, if any, should be made in sentence 9?

    F Change *Altho* to **Although**

    G Change *his* to **he**

    H Change *worked* to **working**

    J Make no change

BE SURE YOU HAVE RECORDED ALL OF YOUR ANSWERS
ON THE ANSWER DOCUMENT.

Grade 5 • Unit 3 • Week 3
Student Evaluation Chart

Tested Skills	Number Correct	Percent Correct
Reading Comprehension: *Compare and Contrast,* 1, 2, 3; *Author's Purpose,* 4	/4	%
Short Answer: *Compare and Contrast,* 9	/3	%
Vocabulary Strategies: *Context Clues:* 5, 7; *Homographs,* 6, 8	/4	%
Spelling: *Words with Vowel Team Syllables,* 11, 14	/2	%
Grammar, Mechanics, and Usage: *Main and Helping Verbs,* 10, 12; *Contractions,* 13	/3	%
Total Weekly Test Score	/16	%

Student Name _____

Date _____

Weekly Assessment

TESTED SKILLS AND STRATEGIES

- **Reading Comprehension**
- **Vocabulary Strategies**
- **Spelling**
- **Grammar, Mechanics, and Usage**

Macmillan/McGraw-Hill

How the Elephant Became an Elephant

1   When the elephant wanted more than anything to become an animal and live on Earth, he decided he wanted to be large and powerful. The elephant's spirit wandered Earth as wind and came upon a large mountain. The mountain was casting a huge shadow on the earth. The elephant picked up the shadow and found that it was heavy, like the mountain. He pulled the shadow over him like a sweater and gave himself a body.

2   The elephant wanted to walk in his new body, but when he tried to move, he was stuck. His shadow-body was like a stone. While it made him as big as he had wanted to be, it did not give him anything to stand on or move with.

3   The elephant thought about what kind of legs he should have and how he would get them. He looked toward the sky, and he noticed that the shadows of the nearby trees were getting longer as the day went by. If I wait long enough, he thought, the shadows will reach me. He <u>proceeded</u> to wait until the shadows reached the ground. Then he chose four thick shadows and picked them up. He propped himself up on his new legs.

4   The elephant decided that he needed to shorten his legs, for they were

© Macmillan/McGraw-Hill

GO ON

as tall as tree trunks! So he started jumping and jumping, and his legs got shorter and shorter until they were just right. Now, however, the skin on his legs was very loose, so he gathered up the extra skin and slung it over his shoulders. His skin was wrinkled and baggy, but it worked just fine. He had extra skin to spare, however, so he gathered up two big flaps, and they became his ears.

5   By and by, the elephant got hungry. He thought about food and trees with delicious leaves and branches. The elephant tried to sniff out the trees with his nose, but his nose was too small! He sniffed harder and harder. To his amazement, the harder he sniffed, the longer his nose grew. Finally it grew so long it reached the trees. He grabbed a branch with a sense of <u>urgency</u> and pulled it back into his mouth. It had the best taste the elephant could imagine!

6   Now it was nighttime and the elephant was happy. He reached his long trunk up into the night sky and trumpeted the most beautiful sound. As he did, his trunk split pieces from the moon and made the moon perfectly round. The elephant gathered up the moon pieces and attached them to either side of his face. These would help him tear down those delicious trees. Finally, the elephant was complete.

GO ON

Page 3

1 One theme of this story shows the value of —

   A loyalty

   B trust

   C patience

   D confidence

2 In this story, the elephant shows the importance of —

   F not giving up

   G relying on others

   H staying close to home

   J not wasting time

3 By the end of the story, the elephant feels more —

   A content

   B brave

   C boastful

   D anxious

4 What happens just after the elephant jumps up and down?

   F His spirit wandered Earth.

   G He is complete.

   H He can not stand or move.

   J His legs are shorter.

5 What does the author mean when he writes, "The elephant's spirit wandered Earth as wind"?

   A The elephant lived in a windy place.

   B The elephant's body was formless, like the wind.

   C The elephant's trunk blows air, just like wind.

   D The elephant was blown into the world by wind.

6 In paragraph 3, what does <u>proceeded</u> mean?

   F Continued

   G Decided

   H Hoped

   J Tried

GO ON

Page 4

7 In sentence 5, what does <u>urgency</u> mean?

   A Showing great strength

   B Being very hungry

   C Having great need

   D Trying to imagine

8 Read these sentences from the story.

The elephant gathered up the moon pieces and attached them to either side of his face. These would help him tear down those delicious trees.

These sentences mean that the moon pieces became the elephant's —

   F ears

   G teeth

   H tusks

   J eyes

9 In this story, how do the elephant's actions show the importance of being resourceful? Explain your answer and support it with details from the story.

_____

_____

_____

_____

_____

_____

_____

Page 5

GO ON ➡

Read the introduction and the passage that follows. Then read each question and fill in the correct answer on your answer document.

Sarah wrote this story for her teacher. She wants you to review her work. As you read, think about the corrections and improvements that Sarah should make. Then answer the questions that follow.

Fox and Stork

(1) One day, sly Fox invited his neighbor, Stork, to his house for dinner. (2) He served her soup in a shallow bowl. (3) Stork tried to dip her long and narrow beak into the bowl to eat, but it was very difficult. (4) Meanwhile, Fox sat at the tabel and lapped up his soup, enjoying every lick.

(5) Stork realized what Fox was doing, so she invited Fox to her house the next night.

(6) For their dinner, Stork prepared a tasty meal of littel bits of shredded meat served in two bottles with long, narrow necks. (7) Fox watched angrily as Stork slid her long thin beak into the glass bottle and ate the delicious meat. (8) Stork looked up from her meal and said, "Fox, it seemed you are not eating very much! (9) Shall I help finish your meal for you?"

(10) Stork, you tricked me! Fox yelled as he stormed off.

Page 6

© Macmillan/McGraw-Hill

10 Which word in sentence 3 is a linking verb?

   F *tried*

   G *dip*

   H *eat*

   J *was*

11 What change, if any, should be made in sentence 4?

   A Change *tabel* to **table**

   B Change *lapped* to **lapping**

   C Change *enjoying* to **enjoyed**

   D Make no change

12 What change, if any, should be made in sentence 6?

   F Change *meal* to **meals**

   G Change *littel* to **little**

   H Change *served* to **serving**

   J Make no change

13 What is the **BEST** way to rewrite sentence 8?

   A Stork looked up from her meal and said, "Fox, it has seemed you are not eating very much!

   B Stork looked up from her meal and said, "Fox, it seeming you are not eating very much!

   C Stork looked up from her meal and said, "Fox, it seems you are not eating very much!

   D Stork looked up from her meal and said, "Fox, it have seems you are not eating very much!

14 What is the **BEST** way to rewrite sentence 10?

   F Stork, "you tricked me!" Fox yelled as he stormed off.

   G "Stork, you tricked me!" Fox yelled as he stormed off.

   H "Stork, you tricked me! Fox yelled as he stormed off."

   J "Stork, you tricked me! Fox yelled" as he stormed off.

© Macmillan/McGraw-Hill

Page 7

BE SURE YOU HAVE RECORDED ALL OF YOUR ANSWERS ON THE ANSWER DOCUMENT.

Grade 5 • Unit 3 • Week 4
Student Evaluation Chart

Tested Skills	Number Correct	Percent Correct
Reading Comprehension: *Theme*, 1,2, 3; *Sequence*, 4	/4	%
Short Answer: *Theme*, 9	/3	%
Vocabulary Strategies: *Figurative Language*, 5, 8; *Context Clues*, 6, 7	/4	%
Spelling: *Words with Consonants + -le Syllables*, 11, 12	/2	%
Grammar, Mechanics, and Usage: *Linking Verbs*, 10, 13; *Quotation Marks in Dialogue*, 14	/3	%
Total Weekly Test Score	**/16**	**%**

Student Name _____

Date _____

Weekly Assessment
TESTED SKILLS AND STRATEGIES

- **Reading Comprehension**
- **Vocabulary Strategies**
- **Spelling**
- **Grammar, Mechanics, and Usage**

Mc Graw Hill Macmillan/McGraw-Hill

To Honor a Hero

1 Martin sat quietly between his mother and his grandfather. The meeting hall was crowded with people who had come to pay their respects to a hero. Martin was confused. When he thought of heroes, people in action movies came to mind. He searched the creased, smiling faces of many of the elderly people sitting around him. But none of them looked much like a hero to him.

2 The speaker started his speech. "Friends, we are here to honor a man who served the Navajo people and the United States of America. This was a man who <u>enlisted</u> in the Marines during World War II. He signed up as a Navajo Code Talker." The speaker looked around the audience. "Some of our youngsters may not know that many Navajo took part with the Marines in every battle in the Pacific Corridor from 1942 to 1945. Our men served in more than one <u>invasion</u>, and they were a crucial part of these attacks."

3 Martin's eyes wandered over the faces of the older men. Did some of them really play such an important role in a war? He wondered about this in disbelief.

4 Martin's shoulders sagged with boredom. He had heard about World War II in school. It belonged to the past. What was so exciting about a war, anyway? People were always fighting. Even on <u>reservation</u> land where everyone lived and worked, people sometimes fought with each other.

5 Martin turned his attention again to the speaker. "The time has come," the man was saying, "to honor our Code Talkers, now that so many of them

GO ON

Page 2

have passed on. These were the people who helped assure victory in the war by sending and receiving coded messages about troop actions and orders. They sent vital information about each battle location so the Allies could position themselves at the site of the action. No member of the enemy Axis forces could break the Navajo Code during the Battle of Iwo Jima, and six of our people worked without sleep until that battle was won."

6   There were murmurs among the crowd, and Martin leaned forward. This was getting more interesting.

7   "A man we know only as a friend and neighbor was a Code Talker," said the speaker. "After the war, he came home to help his people on the reservation. He did not forget his home, and so he will not be forgotten."

8   Then a surprising thing happened. The speaker asked Martin's grandfather to rise. "Let us honor one of our Code Talkers."

9   Martin glanced at his mom. There were tears in her eyes. He felt a tightening in his chest as he looked up at the man he thought he knew so well. His own grandfather—a hero!

---

1 Look at the diagram of information from the story.

Which of these belongs on the blank line?

A The author believes Code Talkers started the war.

B The author believes Code Talkers should be celebrated.

C The author believes Code Talkers are only elderly people.

D The author believes Code Talkers should be in action movies.

Page 3

GO ON

2 The author believes that the Navajo Code Talkers —

F were braver than the Marines

G made important contributions to the war

H had the most dangerous role in the war

J should have been honored sooner than they were

3 The author wants the reader to understand that —

A Martin's grandfather was a modest and heroic man

B Martin's grandfather was the best Code Talker of all

C war always leads to victory

D war is boring and belongs in the past

4 With which statement below would the author most likely agree?

F Martin is right to be proud of his grandfather.

G Martin is right to be bored by a war from the distant past.

H Martin's grandfather should be ashamed of how Martin was acting.

J Martin's grandfather should have shared the secret codes with Martin.

5 In paragraph 2, the word <u>enlisted</u> means —

A signed up

B attracted

C spoke for

D engineered

6 Which word in paragraph 2 helps the reader understand what <u>invasion</u> means?

F *part*

G *men*

H *served*

J *attacks*

Page 4

GO ON

7 Which word in paragraph 4 helps the reader understand what <u>reservation</u> means?

    A *land*

    B *worked*

    C *people*

    D *fought*

8 In paragraph 5, what does the word <u>location</u> mean?

    F Code

    G Place

    H Result

    J Group

9 Why were the Code Talkers important in World War II? Explain your answer and support it with details from the story.

_____

_____

_____

_____

_____

_____

_____

Page 5

GO ON ▶

DIRECTIONS

Read the introduction and the passage that follows. Then read each question and fill in the correct answer on your answer document.

Matt wrote this essay. He wants you to review his work. As you read, think about the corrections and improvements that Matt should make. Then answer the questions that follow.

Turn Off the TV!

(1) Twenty years ago, most American kids spended a lot less time watching TV than they do today. (2) Many of those kids of 20 years ago being more active than most of today's kids. (3) Is there a strong connection between these two facts? (4) Whether there's a connection or not, here's some advice: Turn off your TV more often! (5) Do something creative with paper, scissirs, and markers. (6) Move your body to music. Learn a new skill. (7) Help your parents with light labor that needs to be done around the house. (8) The most important thing is to became more active. (9) There is a lot more to do in the world than to watch television!

Weekly Assessment

© Macmillan/McGraw-Hill

10 What change, if any, should be made in sentence 1?

   F Change *kids* to **kid's**

   G Change *spended* to **spent**

   H Change *watching* to **watch**

   J Make no change

11 What change, if any, should be made in sentence 2?

   A Change *those* to **them**

   B Change *being* to **were**

   C Change *today's* to **todays**

   D Make no change

12 What change, if any, should be made in sentence 5?

   F Change *do* to **does**

   G Take out the comma after *paper*

   H Change *scissirs* to **scissors**

   J Make no change

13 What change, if any, should be made in sentence 7?

   A Change *Help* to **Helps**

   B Change *your* to **you're**

   C Change *labor* to **laber**

   D Make no change

14 What change, if any, should be made in sentence 8?

   F Change *most* to **mostly**

   G Change *became* to **become**

   H Change *more* to **most**

   J Make no change

Page 7

BE SURE YOU HAVE RECORDED ALL OF YOUR ANSWERS ON THE ANSWER DOCUMENT.

Grade 5 • Unit 3 • Week 5
Student Evaluation Chart

Tested Skills	Number Correct	Percent Correct
Reading Comprehension: *Author's Perspective*, 1, 2, 3, 4	/4	%
Short Answer: *Draw Conclusions*, 9	/3	%
Vocabulary Strategies: *Context Clues*, 5, 6, 7, 8	/4	%
Spelling: *Words with r-Controlled Vowels*, 12, 13	/2	%
Grammar, Mechanics, and Usage: *Irregular Verbs*, 10; *Correct Verb Usage*, 11, 14	/3	%
Total Weekly Test Score	**/16**	**%**

Student Name _____

Date _____

Weekly Assessment

TESTED SKILLS AND STRATEGIES

- **Reading Comprehension**
- **Vocabulary Strategies**
- **Spelling**
- **Grammar, Mechanics, and Usage**

Macmillan/McGraw-Hill

Roald Amundsen, Polar Explorer

1   Roald Amundsen was a famous polar explorer. In 1897, Amundsen joined an <u>expedition</u> that made scientific investigations in Antarctica. In 1903, he became the first European to travel the Northwest Passage.

2   Amundsen had dreamed of being the first European to reach the North Pole, but Robert E. Peary got there first. As a result, Amundsen abandoned the idea of an expedition to the North Pole and began planning one to the South Pole instead. He kept this plan secret because he did not want Robert Falcon Scott's team to know what he was doing. Scott also was planning an expedition to the South Pole, and Amundsen did not want him to know that he had competition.

3   Amundsen's ship, the *Fram*, left Norway on August 9, 1910, eight weeks after the departure of Scott's team. On board were 97 Greenland sled dogs.

© Macmillan/McGraw-Hill

Page 2

Amundsen believed that sled dogs would be more effective than the ponies and tractors with motors that Scott used to pull his sledges. The *Fram* also carried a hut and enough supplies to last the crew for two years. The supplies included lamps, food, tools, and medicines for the treatment of injuries.

4 Four months later, the *Fram* reached the Ross Ice Shelf in Antarctica. The men built their base camp at the Bay of Whales. Because the team members would need supplies and shelter along the route to the South Pole, they set up depots, or storage places for supplies, along the way. The labor was difficult and demanding, and the men had to finish their tasks as fast as they could. They were in a race against time. The long, dark nights of winter would begin in April. Amundsen also worried about Scott's team reaching the South Pole before him.

5 On September 8, the team of eight men started off over the treacherous ice with sledges that were pulled by 86 dogs. One man stayed behind to watch over their base camp. Frigid weather set in, so the team made a run for the nearest depot. The weather was so cold that the team had to return to the base camp. As soon as the weather improved, a smaller group started out again. Amundsen and four other men struggled through blizzards and over glaciers. They were determined to beat Scott's expedition, despite the delay that the terrible weather had caused.

6 Finally, on December 14, 1911, Amundsen and his men reached the uninhabited South Pole. The team members planted the Norwegian flag in the frozen ground to celebrate their victory over Scott and the harsh conditions they had endured along the way.

GO ON

Page 3

1 What problem made Amundsen decide to go to the South Pole instead of the North Pole?

   A His competitor found out he was planning to go to the North Pole.

   B Someone else had already made it to the North Pole.

   C The North Pole was too far away.

   D The North Pole had very harsh weather conditions.

2 Which problem did Amundsen face in his exploration of the South Pole?

   F Another explorer found out about his plans.

   G He was unable to find eight experienced men for his team.

   H He ran out of supplies for the trip to the South Pole.

   J Another explorer was trying to reach the South Pole first.

3 In paragraph 1, what does expedition mean?

   A A big decision

   B An experiment

   C An athletic activity for a large group

   D A trip made for a purpose

4 In paragraph 5, treacherous means —

   F without danger

   G one who faces danger

   H having many dangers

   J able to face danger

5 In paragraph 5, what does the word frigid mean?

   A Freezing

   B Windy

   C Unsettled

   D Dangerous

6 In paragraph 6, uninhabited means —

   F not inhabited

   G a person who inhabits

   H the process of inhabiting

   J inhabit again

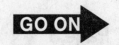

Weekly Assessment

7 What helped Amundsen succeed in reaching the South Pole before Scott?

  A Building a base camp

  B Starting the trip before Scott

  C Getting help from Scott's team

  D Using sled dogs for transportation

8 What problem did Amundsen and his team face in September, 1911?

  F Robert E. Peary reached the North Pole first.

  G The long and dark nights made travel impossible.

  H Very cold weather slowed down the team's progress.

  J The team's base camp was difficult to set up.

9 Why did Amundsen and his team set up depots between their base camp and their destination? Explain your answer and support it with details from the article.

_____

_____

_____

_____

_____

_____

_____

Page 5

GO ON ▶

DIRECTIONS

Read the introduction and the passage that follows. Then read each question and fill in the correct answer on your answer document.

Ross wrote this story for his teacher. He wants you to review his work. As you read, think about the corrections and improvements that Ross should make. Then answer the questions that follow.

A Dangerous Journey

(1) The group of men knew they had a long climb ahead of him. (2) Them packed up the last remaining items in their camp and began the journey. (3) This was the tenth day of a long climb up the massive mountan in Asia known as K2. (4) As they began their climb, the weather became worse. (5) The wind picked up and snow began to fall. (6) The men realized it was impossible for them to continue going forward. (7) The captin of the journey decided it was time to stop for the day. (8) The men set up camp and waited out the storm.

Page 6

GO ON

10 What change, if any, should be made in sentence 1?

    F Change *men* to **mens**

    G Change *had* to **have**

    H Change *him* to **them**

    J Make no change

11 What change, if any, should be made in sentence 2?

    A Change *Them* to **They**

    B Change *packed* to **packs**

    C Change *began* to **beginned**

    D Make no change

12 What change, if any, should be made in sentence 3?

    F Change *day* to **days**

    G Change *mountan* to **mountain**

    H Change *Asia* to **asia**

    J Make no change

13 What change, if any, should be made in sentence 6?

    A Change *realized* to **realizing**

    B Change *it* to **he**

    C Change *going* to **go**

    D Make no change

14 What change, if any, should be made in sentence 7?

    F Change *captin* to **captain**

    G Change *decided* to **decide**

    H Change *was* to **were**

    J Make no change

BE SURE YOU HAVE RECORDED ALL OF YOUR ANSWERS ON THE ANSWER DOCUMENT.

Student Name _____

Grade 5 • Unit 4 • Week 1
Student Evaluation Chart

Tested Skills	Number Correct	Percent Correct
Reading Comprehension: *Problem and Solution, 1, 2, 7, 8*	/4	%
Short Answer: *Problem and Solution, 9*	/3	%
Vocabulary Strategies: *Context Clues, 3, 5; Word Parts: Suffixes, 4; Word Parts: Prefixes, 6*	/4	%
Spelling: *Words with final /əl/ and /ən/, 12, 14*	/2	%
Grammar, Mechanics, and Usage: *Pronoun-Antecendent Agreement, 10; Pronouns and Antecedents, 11, 13*	/3	%
Total Weekly Test Score	/16	%

Student Name _____

Date _____

Weekly Assessment

TESTED SKILLS AND STRATEGIES

- **Reading Comprehension**
- **Vocabulary Strategies**
- **Spelling**
- **Grammar, Mechanics, and Usage**

Mc Graw Hill Macmillan/McGraw-Hill

Exploring Space with Satellites

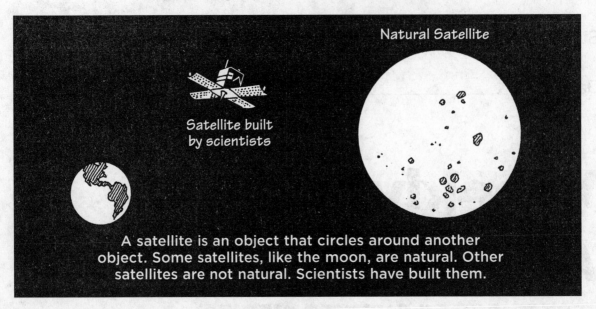

A satellite is an object that circles around another object. Some satellites, like the moon, are natural. Other satellites are not natural. Scientists have built them.

1   People have always been interested in outer space. They have looked with wonder at the night sky. Long ago the Egyptians looked to the stars to predict floods. The early Greeks studied the moon and stars to create a calendar.

2   Today we know much more about space. For more than 40 years, scientists have sent astronauts into space to explore. Astronauts get to space in rockets that break the grip of Earth's gravity. Gravity is the force that draws objects toward the center of Earth. The atmosphere, a zone of gasses surrounding Earth, is held in place by gravity. Without gravity the environment on Earth would not be like it is today. Gravity makes Earth's air, water, plants, and animals possible.

3   Scientists do not just send people into space. They also send special machines, which are called satellites. Sometimes you can see satellites after dark. They move across the night sky and look like blinking lights.

4   Some satellites explore space, just as astronauts do. They may study the moon, sun, and stars. They may be sent to other planets. For example, a satellite took photos of Jupiter in 1979. These photos showed that Jupiter's great red spot is a huge storm. Other satellites explored Saturn's rings and

© Macmillan/McGraw-Hill

GO ON

Page 2

5   moons. In 1997, a satellite was sent to Mars. It studied the planet's weather and land by taking photos. Some satellites study our own planet. They send information to computers. Some scientists use the information to study oceans. Others use it to make maps.

5   Not all satellites have the <u>mission</u> of exploring space. The job of some satellites is to carry signals over long distances. They carry TV, radio, and telephone signals. Some of the earliest satellites had this purpose. The first telephone and TV satellite went into space in 1962.

6   Other satellites locate objects on Earth. They might locate ships, planes, or even cars. For this to happen, the object must have a special receiver.

7   Another kind of satellite studies weather. These satellites take photos of clouds and storms. They send this information to computers on Earth. The information helps scientists predict the weather. Weather satellites also were an early kind of satellite. The first one went into space in 1960.

8   Scientists work hard to avoid having problems with satellites. They plan for a long time. But disasters can happen. Some satellites fall out of orbit. Others get lost in the <u>maze</u> of space. Others simply do not <u>function</u>, so they are useless. Sometimes these satellites are adjusted or replaced.

9   In spite of these problems, scientists keep sending satellites into space. Satellites are our eyes in the sky.

1 What is the main idea of the first illustration and its caption?

A Scientists build satellites.

B The moon is a natural satellite.

C Some objects in the night sky circle around other objects.

D Some satellites are natural, and some are built by scientists.

2 This article is mostly about how satellites —

F perform several different jobs

G Were used 40 years ago.

H send information to computers on Earth

J sometimes have problems and must be replaced

GO ON ➤

Page 3

3 Look at the web of information from the article.

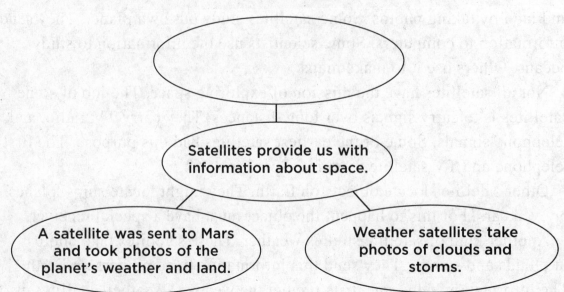

Satellites provide us with information about space.

A satellite was sent to Mars and took photos of the planet's weather and land.

Weather satellites take photos of clouds and storms.

Which of the following belongs in the empty oval?

A Satellites look like blinking lights in the night sky.

B Satellites explored Saturn's rings and moons.

C Satellites carry TV, radio, and telephone signals.

D Satellites are natural or have been built by scientists.

---

4 In paragraph 5, which word helps the reader understand the meaning of mission?

F *exploring*

G *job*

H *satellites*

J *carry*

5 Which words in paragraph 8 help the reader understand the meaning of maze?

A *work hard*

B *fall out of orbit*

C *get lost*

D *are useless*

© Macmillan/McGraw-Hill

Page 4

6 In paragraph 2, the word <u>zone</u> means —

   F an object

   G an area

   H a satellite

   J a rocket

7 In paragraph 8, what does the word <u>function</u> mean?

   A Work correctly

   B Travel fast

   C Become lost

   D Be replaced

8 Which statement best supports the idea that scientists work hard to avoid having problems with satellites?

   F Weather satellites were early satellites.

   G Some satellites have to be replaced.

   H Scientists plan for a long time.

   J Some satellites fall out of orbit.

9 What is gravity, and why is it important? Explain your answer and support it with details from the article.

_____

_____

_____

_____

_____

_____

GO ON →

Page 5

DIRECTIONS

Read the introduction and the passage that follows. Then read each question and fill in the correct answer on your answer document.

Megan wrote this story in her journal. She wants you to review her work. As you read, think about the corrections and improvements that Megan should make. Then answer the questions that follow.

First Time

(1) Jaycee arrived at the beach with her family and felt a rush of excitement. (2) She was going snorkeling for the first time! (3) She couldn't wait to see the colorful fish. (4) Maybe she'd even see a leatherback a large turtle found in the Caribbean while she explored the cove. (5) First, she picked up the flippers for her feet, goggles, and a snorkel tube. (6) Without the tube, she would be unable to breathe while she was underwater. (7) Jacyee tried to put on the equipment, but her was having a hard time with the flippers. (8) Her dad said it would be easier to submurge her feet in the water while trying to put them on. (9) His advice worked, and she got the flippers on as Mom and Dad waited. (10) Then she waved to they and walked into the sea.

© Macmillan/McGraw-Hill

GO ON ➡

Page 6

10 What is the **BEST** way to rewrite sentence 4?

F Maybe she'd even see a leatherback. A large turtle found in the Caribbean while she explored the cove.

G Maybe she'd even see a leatherback, a large turtle found in the Caribbean, while she explored the cove.

H Maybe she'd even see a leatherback, a large turtle found in the Caribbean while she explored the cove.

J Maybe she'd even see a leatherback, a large turtle found in the Caribbean. While she explored the cove.

11 What change, if any, should be made in sentence 6?

A Change *unable* to **nonable**

B Change *she* to **her**

C Change *underwater* to **underwatter**

D Make no change

12 What change, if any, should be made in sentence 7?

F Change *tried* to **trying**

G Take out the comma after *equipment*

H Change *her* to **she**

J Make no change

13 What change, if any, should be made in sentence 8?

A Change *dad* to **Dad**

B Change *submurge* to **submerge**

C Change *them* to **it**

D Make no change

14 What change, if any, should be made in sentence 10?

F Change *she* to **her**

G Change *waved* to **waving**

H Change *they* to **them**

J Make no change

BE SURE YOU HAVE RECORDED ALL OF YOUR ANSWERS ON THE ANSWER DOCUMENT.

Grade 5 • Unit 4 • Week 2
Student Evaluation Chart

Tested Skills	Number Correct	Percent Correct
Reading Comprehension: *Main Idea and Details,* 1, 2, 3, 8	/4	%
Short Answer: *Main Idea and Details,* 9	/3	%
Vocabulary Strategies: *Context Clues,* 4, 5, 6, 7	/4	%
Spelling: *Words with Prefixes,* 11, 13	/2	%
Grammar, Mechanics, and Usage: *Appositives,* 10; *Subject and Object Pronouns,* 12, 14	/3	%
Total Weekly Test Score	/16	%

Student Name _____

Date _____

Weekly Assessment

TESTED SKILLS AND STRATEGIES

- **Reading Comprehension**
- **Vocabulary Strategies**
- **Spelling**
- **Grammar, Mechanics, and Usage**

Mc Graw Hill **Macmillan/McGraw-Hill**

Democracy in the United States

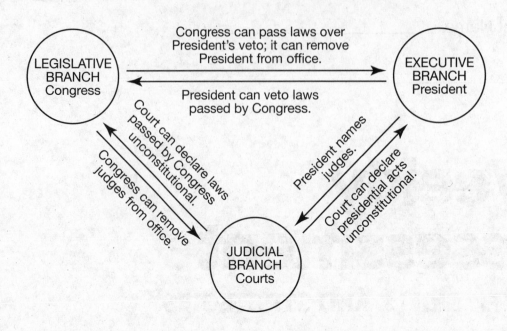

1   The United States is a <u>democracy</u>. Democracy is an excellent form of government. It is a government for the people. In a democracy, the people choose their leaders by voting. The leaders then share the responsibility of leading the country.

2   Not all countries are democracies. In some places, a king or a queen rules the country. These kinds of leaders are born into ruling families. The people who wrote the Constitution of the United States set up a democracy because they wanted their government to be different. It takes many people working together to make a government work well.

3   The U.S. government has three parts, or "branches." One is the executive branch. This branch includes the President and the cabinet. The President's cabinet is made up of people who advise the President. They help the President deal with problems in the country and in the world. The President and the cabinet members work together as a team to make important decisions and carry out the laws.

GO ON

Page 2

4   The legislative branch of government creates the laws. The main part of this branch is called Congress. Congress is made up of two groups of people that form the Senate and the House of Representatives. These people represent every state in the nation. Members of each group work together to create ideas for laws, called bills. Then the two groups work together to turn those bills into laws.

5   The third branch of government is the judicial branch. It includes the Supreme Court. The Supreme Court has a team of nine justices. These judges explain the laws and decide when people have broken them. To do their jobs, the judges must understand the Constitution. They must decide how the laws of the Constitution apply to certain situations.

6   Though each branch of the government has its own leaders, these branches must work together to make a democracy work. Each branch of government must check the actions of the other two branches. This prevents one person or one team of people from having too much power.

7   The U.S. government has survived for more than 200 years. But it takes more than good leaders for a democracy to live on. The people of the country must get involved in the government, too. In the United States, citizens may vote when they reach 18 years of age. Then they can help elect the country's leaders. They can vote for the President of the United States. They can also vote for leaders who represent their states in Congress. People who participate affect the whole country. They have an impact on what happens in the United States of America.

1 Which sentence from the article is an opinion?

   A *Democracy is an excellent form of government.*

   B *The President's cabinet is made up of people who advise the President.*

   C *The legislative branch of government creates the laws.*

   D *In the United States, citizens may vote when they reach 18 years of age.*

2 Which sentence is a fact?

   F The government of the United States works well.

   G Other countries have problems because they do not have democracies.

   H The U.S. government has three branches.

   J Having only one leader causes problems in a government.

3 People in Congress have to —

   A make sure U.S. citizens vote

   B represent the states

   C work on the Supreme Court

   D lead the executive branch

4 What is the main idea of this article?

   F There are three branches of government in the United States.

   G Congress creates the laws in the United States.

   H Many people work together to make democracy work in the United States.

   J Many other countries are not democracies.

5 In paragraph 1, the word democracy comes from a Greek root that means —

   A people

   B ruler

   C judge

   D family

© Macmillan/McGraw-Hill

GO ON

Page 4

6 In paragraph 7, the word <u>survived</u> comes from a Latin root that means —

   F write

   G live

   H break

   J see

7 In paragraph 7, the word <u>involved</u> means —

   A taking part in

   B learning about

   C getting advice from

   D trying to make better

8 In paragraph 7, what does the word <u>impact</u> mean?

   F Purpose

   G Chance

   H Desire

   J Influence

9 What facts in the article explain the responsibilities of the judicial branch of government? Explain your answer and support it with details from the article.

_____

_____

_____

_____

_____

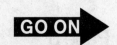

Page 5

DIRECTIONS

Read the introduction and the passage that follows. Then read each question and fill in the correct answer on your answer document.

April wrote this essay. She wants you to review her work. As you read, think about the corrections and improvements that April should make. Then answer the questions that follow.

Our Country's Young Citizens

(1) United States citizens play an important role in our country. (2) Citizens vote for our leaders, and they can work with our government. (3) For many years, only people age 21 and over could vote. (4) In 1972, an important law was passed by the US government. (5) This law purmits people 18 years old and over to vote. (6) No matter what your age, however, there are many things you can do to help your country work better. (7) You can learns facts about events that are happening in the world and form opinions about your country's problems and how to solve them. (8) You can conduckt yourself responsibly by thinking about how your actions affect others. (9) It is also important to take care of the environment. (10) No matter what your age, you can do your part.

Page 6

GO ON ➡

10 What change, if any, should be made in sentence 4?

    F Change *law* to **laws**

    G Change *passed* to **past**

    H Change *US* to **U.S.**

    J Make no change

11 What change, if any, should be made in sentence 5?

    A Change *This* to **These**

    B Change *purmits* to **permits**

    C Change *vote* to **voting**

    D Make no change

12 What change, if any, should be made in sentence 6?

    F Change *there* to **their**

    G Change *you* to **us**

    H Change *work* to **works**

    J Make no change

13 What change, if any, should be made in sentence 7?

    A Change *learns* to **learn**

    B Change *are* to **is**

    C Change *country's* to **countries**

    D Make no change

14 What change, if any, should be made in sentence 8?

    F Change *conduckt* to **conduct**

    G Change *thinking* to **thought**

    H Change *your* to **yours**

    J Make no change

BE SURE YOU HAVE RECORDED ALL OF YOUR ANSWERS
ON THE ANSWER DOCUMENT.

Student Name _____

Grade 5 • Unit 4 • Week 3
Student Evaluation Chart

Tested Skills	Number Correct	Percent Correct
Reading Comprehension: *Fact and Opinion*, 1, 2; *Main Idea and Details*, 3, 4	/4	%
Short Answer: *Fact and Opinion*, 9	/3	%
Vocabulary Strategies: *Greek and Latin Roots*, 5, 6; *Context Clues*, 7, 8	/4	%
Spelling: *Homographs*, 11, 14	/2	%
Grammar, Mechanics, and Usage: *Abbreviations*, 10; *Pronoun-Verb Agreement*, 12, 13	/3	%
Total Weekly Test Score	**/16**	**%**

Student Name _____

Date _____

Weekly Assessment

TESTED SKILLS AND STRATEGIES

- **Reading Comprehension**
- **Vocabulary Strategies**
- **Spelling**
- **Grammar, Mechanics, and Usage**

Macmillan/McGraw-Hill

A Saturday Morning Adventure

1   "These new video games are really cool," Rasheed says. He and his friend Jami play video games almost every weekend. They like the games that take place in outer space the best. They put on spacesuits and climb into a space pod. Then they fight battles against other spaceships and aliens.

2   On this particular Saturday, the two kids are playing "Space Attack." In this game, meteors zoom from outer space into Earth's atmosphere, and attack ships try to hit the players' ship.

3   "Look," Jami says. "I just reversed course. Maybe if I go the opposite way my spaceship won't get smashed. It's a good thing we have our spacesuits on. If our ship gets hit by a meteor, we can just float through space until a robot rescues us."

4   "To continue playing for an additional minute, please pay 100 more tokens at this time," says the robot running the game room.

5   "Will do," says Rasheed, and he hands the robot the tokens. The machine looks just like a real person. "These new robots can do anything. They're so much better than the old-fashioned robots of the last century."

6   "You can say that again," says Jami. "My grandfather told me stories about the robots that people used when he was young. They had jerky

Page 2

GO ON

movements, and they talked in a funny way. My grandfather makes me laugh when he imitates them."

7   Suddenly, Rasheed screams, "Look out! That attack ship just <u>rotated</u> and turned around. Now it's headed right toward us!"

8   Jami calmly pulls up on her joystick. "This is easy," she says with a laugh. But her laugh is cut off by the gasp she makes when the joystick fails to respond. "This joystick is <u>defective</u>!" she yells. "The attack ship is gaining on us!"

9   Rasheed adjusts the dials to increase their speed, but the ship still can't move fast enough to avoid the attack. With a sickening thud, the attack ship hits theirs. Jami is thrown forward and then staggers back into her seat. Suddenly, Rasheed finds himself <u>dangling</u> from the ceiling. He holds tightly onto his seat belt, and sways like a spider on its web.

10   But Jami doesn't panic. She checks to make sure that her spacesuit hasn't been damaged. Next, she asks Rasheed if he's hurt and tells him to check his spacesuit. Then, she calmly takes out her tools. She repairs the joystick and adjusts the dials. "All fixed," she announces. She calmly steers the ship into dock.

11   When the kids climb out of their own space pod, Rasheed makes a suggestion. "Maybe next week we can go laser-bowling instead of playing video games."

12   "No way!" Jami says. "Compared to these new video games, laser-bowling is way too boring!"

GO ON

Page 3

1   What can the reader conclude about the game "Space Attack"?

   A It is inexpensive to play.

   B It makes battles seem real.

   C It is easy to win.

   D It was created by aliens.

2   Which sentence best describes Jami?

   F She stays calm under pressure.

   G She sometimes jumps to conclusions.

   H She often panics in difficult situations.

   J She needs more practice repairing things.

3   What happens just before the attack ship turns around and heads for Jami and Rasheed's ship?

   A Rasheed pays the robot.

   B Jami steers the ship into the dock.

   C Rasheed increases the speed.

   D Jami tells a story about her grandfather.

4   Based on the events in the story, what can the reader conclude about Jami and Rasheed?

   F Jami likes adventure more than Rasheed does.

   G Rasheed likes to be in charge more than Jami does.

   H Jami and Rasheed have been friends for many years.

   J Rasheed and Jami often disagree on how to solve a problem.

5   Which word best completes the analogy? Tokens are to coins as caps are to —

   A heads

   B games

   C hats

   D balls

6   Which words in paragraph 7 help the reader understand the meaning of rotated?

   F *look out*

   G *attack ship*

   H *turned around*

   J *headed right*

© Macmillan/McGraw-Hill

GO ON

Page 4

7 Which word best completes the analogy? Additional is to more as defective is to —

   A confusing

   B broken

   C slow

   D difficult

8 In paragraph 9, what does the word dangling mean?

   F Watching closely

   G Hanging loosely

   H Trying harder

   J Moving faster

9 What kind of person is Rasheed? Explain your answer and support it with details from the story.

_____

_____

_____

_____

_____

_____

Page 5

GO ON

DIRECTIONS

Read the introduction and the passage that follows. Then read each question and fill in the correct answer on your answer document.

Manny wrote this story. He wants you to review his work. As you read, think about the corrections and improvements that Manny should make. Then answer the questions that follow.

A Hurt Student

(1) Jessie ran into the nurse's office and cried, "Christie, my six year old sister, fell down the stairs and hurt herself!"

(2) Ms. Shapiro, the school nurse, stayed calm. (3) She got some supplies and said, "Take me to Christie."

(4) They went to the stairwell where Christie was lying on the floor. (5) The nurse bent down and began to ask Christie questions. (6) Then she gently moved her leg and said, "It's a sprain, but it's not a fracture. (7) Let's get a strecher so she doesn't have to walk on it."

(8) The kids who saw what happened wanted to help Christie. (9) "These books are she's," Joseph said, scooping up Christie's books. (10) "I'll carry them."

(11) Keiko bent down and picked up a necklace near the stairs and asked Christie, "Is this your?"

(12) Christie said yes and thanked her friends for helping her.

10 What change, if any, should be made in sentence 1?

    F Change *nurse's* to **nurses**

    G Change *six year old* to **six-year-old**

    H Change *hurt* to **hurted**

    J Make no change

11 What change, if any, should be made in sentence 6?

    A Change *her* to **hers**

    B Change *It's* to **Its**

    C Change *fracture* to **frackture**

    D Make no change

12 What change, if any, should be made in sentence 7?

    F Change *Let's* to **Lets**

    G Change *strecher* to **stretcher**

    H Change *it* to **them**

    J Make no change

13 What change, if any, should be made in sentence 9?

    A Take out the quotation marks

    B Change *she's* to **hers**

    C Change *said* to **sayed**

    D Make no change

14 What change, if any, should be made in sentence 11?

    F Change *bent* to **bended**

    G Change *asked* to **asking**

    H Change *your* to **yours**

    J Make no change

Page 7

BE SURE YOU HAVE RECORDED ALL OF YOUR ANSWERS ON THE ANSWER DOCUMENT.

Grade 5 • Unit 4 • Week 4
Student Evaluation Chart

Tested Skills	Number Correct	Percent Correct
Reading Comprehension: *Draw Conclusions, 1, 2, 4; Sequence, 3*	/4	%
Short Answer: *Draw Conclusions, 9*	/3	%
Vocabulary Strategies: *Analogies: Synonyms, 5, 7; Context Clues, 6, 8*	/4	%
Spelling: *Words with /chər/ and /zhər/, 11, 12*	/2	%
Grammar, Mechanics, and Usage: *Use Hyphens, 10; Possessive Pronouns, 13, 14*	/3	%
Total Weekly Test Score	/16	%

© Macmillan/McGraw-Hill

Student Name _____

Date _____

Weekly Assessment

TESTED SKILLS AND STRATEGIES

- **Reading Comprehension**
- **Vocabulary Strategies**
- **Spelling**
- **Grammar, Mechanics, and Usage**

Macmillan/McGraw-Hill

Camping Out

1   "This tent was supposed to be really straightforward to put together," Randall told Nick as he scattered tent poles on the ground. "It was guaranteed to be uncomplicated enough for a child to set up. I'm in the fifth grade, and I guess you could still call me a child. But I can't figure it out." His voice was steadily getting louder. "My dad should demand our money back for this tent." He kicked one of the poles and yelled. "I'm really frustrated, and I'm going to tell my dad to let the manufacturer know about it!" He finished his speech by stomping the ground.

2   Randall, Nick, and their families were camping at a state park. The boys had convinced their parents to let them set up their own campsite a short distance from where everyone else would be. It was a clear October day. The leaves were beginning to turn gold and red, the sun was shining, and birds were chirping joyfully.

3   "Stop yanking on the cords," Nick suggested. "When my mom gets back from her hike, I'll ask her to supervise us. She's an expert at assembling tents. With her help we'll have our campsite set up in a flash."

© Macmillan/McGraw-Hill

Page 2

GO ON ➤

4   Randall ignored Nick and continued to hurl parts of the tent around. Then he barked, "Where did I put that <u>bundle</u>? You know the one I need— it has all the cords and hooks inside it." He stormed around for a minute until he found the bag. But when he opened it, he discovered that all the tape had melted together.

5   "This is the last straw!" he screamed. "All the tape has <u>fused</u>." He threw down the bag and sat on the ground. "Why do people ever go camping? I should have stayed home and played video games. Even doing my math homework or cleaning my room would have been more fun than this."

6   "Relax, Randall," Nick said, sitting down beside his friend. "Look at the scenery. This time of year it's really impressive."

7   "Scenery?" Randall bellowed. "Trees and hills? Who wants to look at that stuff? And what's with all these bugs? This place is crawling with them."

8   Then, after a moment, the look on Randall's face softened a bit. His voice was much quieter when he said, "I don't really like nature. In fact, it makes me feel tense and nervous."

9   "Gee, I never would have thought that," said Nick with a slight smile. "Look, here comes Mom. She can't do anything about the bugs, but she'll help us with the tent. Then next on the schedule is roasting hot dogs."

10   For the first time since they had arrived, Randall smiled. "Come to think of it," he said, "I'm starved."

---

1 In paragraph 1, what does the word <u>guaranteed</u> mean?

  A Questioned

  B Promised

  C Made known

  D Kicked over

2 In paragraph 1, the word <u>frustrated</u> means —

  F upset

  G sad

  H surprised

  J confused

GO ON

Page 3

3 Look at the web of information from the story. Which of these belongs in the empty oval?

   A Randall looks for the bundle of cords.

   B Randall throws the bag down.

   C Randall likes to play video games.

   D Randall is camping at a state park.

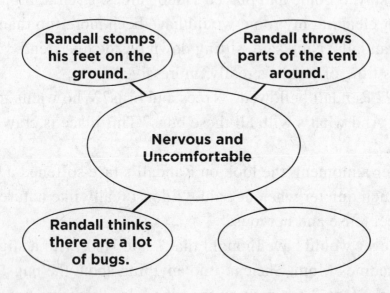

4 In the first part of the story, Randall is —

   F hoping to go home soon

   G trying to hide what is bothering him

   H wishing that he and Nick were not friends

   J hoping Nick's mom will return soon

5 Which sentence best describes Nick?

   A He is a kind and calm person.

   B He is shy and unsure of himself.

   C He likes to take the lead.

   D He likes to solve problems.

6 When this story takes place, the weather is —

F bright and sunny

G dark and stormy

H cold and wet

J hot and humid

7 In paragraph 4, which meaning of the word <u>bundle</u> best fits the way it is used in the story?

A To wrap things together

B A great deal of money

C A group of muscle fibers

D A package of things

8 In paragraph 5, which meaning of <u>fuse</u> best fits the way it is used in the story?

F To melt together

G A cord or string that burns

H To become close friends

J A strip of metal in an electrical circuit

9 Why is camping an unpleasant experience for Randall? Explain your answer and support it with details from the story.

_____

_____

_____

_____

_____

_____

Page 5

GO ON ➡

DIRECTIONS

Read the introduction and the passage that follows. Then read each question and fill in the correct answer on your answer document.

Ben wrote this story. He wants you to review his work. As you read, think about the corrections and improvements that Ben should make. Then answer the questions that follow.

Aunt Cecilia's Farm

(1) Belinda and her dad arrived at Aunt Cecilia's residence, a farm outside of town. (2) Her dad drove their car down the bumpy dirt drive to the farmhouse. (3) Belinda had to smile. (4) A horse-drawn cart was coming down the road, and a donkey was next to it.

(5) Suddenly, the car came to a screeching halt. (6) Dad had also been looking out the window and almost ran into three goats crossing her aunts driveway!

(7) "Dad, you know the importance of always keeping your eyes on the road," Belinda said as she wagged her finger at him. (8) Then she saw her aunt standing in the doorway as them parked the car. (9) Belinda could'nt wait to see her!

Page 6

GO ON

10 What change, if any, should be made in sentence 1?

   F Change *arrived* to **arived**

   G Change *Aunt Cecilia's* to **Aunt Cecilias**

   H Change *residance* to **residence**

   J Make no change

11 What change, if any, should be made in sentence 6?

   A Change *had* to **have**

   B Change *ran* to **run**

   C Change *aunts* to **aunt's**

   D Make no change

12 What change, if any, should be made in sentence 7?

   F Change *know* to **no**

   G Change *importance* to **importence**

   H Change *your* to **you're**

   J Make no change

13 What change, if any, should be made in sentence 8?

   A Change *her* to **hers**

   B Change *them* to **they**

   C Change *parked* to **parks**

   D Make no change

14 What change, if any, should be made in sentence 9?

   F Change *could'nt* to **couldn't**

   G Change *wait* to **weight**

   H Change *her* to **she**

   J Make no change

BE SURE YOU HAVE RECORDED ALL OF YOUR ANSWERS ON THE ANSWER DOCUMENT.

Student Name _____

Grade 5 • Unit 4 • Week 5
Student Evaluation Chart

Tested Skills	Number Correct	Percent Correct
Reading Comprehension: *Character and Setting, 3, 4, 5, 6*	/4	%
Short Answer: *Character and Setting, 9*	/3	%
Vocabulary Strategies: *Multiple-Meaning Words, 7, 8; Context Clues, 1, 2*	/4	%
Spelling: *Words with -ance and -ence, 10, 12*	/2	%
Grammar, Mechanics, and Usage: *Apostrophes and Possessives, 11; Pronouns, 13; Contractions, 14*	/3	%
Total Weekly Test Score	**/16**	**%**

© Macmillan/McGraw-Hill

Student Name _____

Date _____

Weekly Assessment

TESTED SKILLS AND STRATEGIES

- **Reading Comprehension**
- **Vocabulary Strategies**
- **Spelling**
- **Grammar, Mechanics, and Usage**

My Days in San Luis Obispo

1   It was the most remarkable thing I had ever seen. It was 25 feet long when it was finished, and it was made of the most beautiful wood from the forests around us. I had come to San Luis Obispo in California with my family just months earlier. We had come to build a mission. It would serve as a farm and a ranch as well as a church. The local Chumash people worked to build the mission. We taught them farming and livestock herding. They gave us shell ornaments and soapstone, and they let me watch them build a canoe.

2   What I remember most about this time was watching one of the <u>eldest</u> men work. The canoe was called a "tomol." I had seen one once before, speeding through the water. Then one day I walked down to the water and saw an old Chumash man building a tomol. I did not speak his language, but I learned to communicate with him. Every day I would go down to the water where he was working. He smiled at me, and he used sign language to let me know that it was okay to watch.

3   When I first arrived at the water, the man took me by surprise. He had already built the heavy floor out of one piece of wood, and he had stacked up planks to make the sides of the canoe. I watched as he glued each row of planks with yap. Yap was a melted mixture of pine sap and hardened tar. After the glue dried, he drilled holes in the planks. Then he tied the boards together with string he made from plant fiber.

© Macmillan/McGraw-Hill

GO ON ➡

Page 2

4   I could hardly wait to get down to the water each morning to watch him work on his <u>projects</u>. I watched as he filled the holes he had drilled with more yap. I watched as he sanded the wood using sandstone and sharkskin. I watched as he painted the canoe, and then he decorated it with designs.

5   I learned a lot about the Chumash while my family was building the mission. I made friends with a young boy who was a bailer on a canoe. Though the canoes were seaworthy, water often seeped in through the cracks. One person in the canoe had the job of bailing out the water as they traveled along on their fishing trips.

6   My new friend was very kind. Once he gave me a beautiful twine basket he had woven himself. He had sewn a symbol on the front of the basket that <u>depicted</u> his family's heritage. His family was helping my family build the mission. It wasn't <u>obvious</u> how he felt about the mission. I couldn't really tell what he was thinking, and I did not know how to ask him. Mostly, we spoke without words. Like the man who built the canoe, he showed me what it was like to live off the land, and he gave me a glimpse of his remarkable life.

---

1 Why did the narrator come to San Luis Obispo?

   A To learn how to build canoes

   B To collect shell ornaments

   C To build a mission

   D To learn a new language

2 The narrator knows it is okay to watch the old Chumash man build the tomol because —

   F his family tells him to do so

   G the man gives him an ornament

   H his new friend works on the tomol

   J the man smiles and makes a sign

Page 3

3 What did the Chumash do when seawater got into their tomols?

   A They tied the boards closer together.

   B They added more planks to the floor of the tomol.

   C They filled the holes with yap, or glue.

   D They had someone in the canoe scoop out the water.

4 The author probably wrote this passage to —

   F describe a personal experience

   G teach readers how to build a tomol

   H explain how the Chumash lived

   J persuade readers to help others

5 In paragraph 2, the word <u>eldest</u> means the same as —

   A tallest

   B finest

   C oldest

   D kindest

6 Which word from a thesaurus means the same as <u>projects</u> in paragraph 4?

   F Extends

   G Launches

   H Pushes

   J Tasks

GO ON

Page 4

7 Which word means about the same as <u>depicted</u> in paragraph 6?

   A Determined

   B Represented

   C Understood

   D Witnessed

8 In paragraph 6, the word <u>obvious</u> means —

   F relaxing to watch

   G pleasant to feel

   H easy to achieve

   J clear to see

9 What did the narrator learn from the Chumash man and the young boy? Explain your answer and support it with details from the article.

_____

_____

_____

_____

_____

_____

_____

Page 5

GO ON ➡

DIRECTIONS

Read the introduction and the passage that follows. Then read each question and fill in the correct answer on your answer document.

Ted wrote this report. He wants you to review his work. As you read, think about the corrections and improvements that Ted should make. Then answer the questions that follow.

The Sonoran Desert

(1) Deserts cover about one-fifth of Earth. (2) There are 12 major deserts in the world. (3) One desert in the United States the Sonoran Desert, covers a large area of southwestern Arizona and southeastern California. (4) The saguaro cactus is a typical plant found in the Sonoran desert. (5) It takes up to 100 years for this cactus to reach maturity. (6) Once it is completeley grown, it can reach up to 25 feet tall. (7) It can be very hot in the desert, and it's not comfortable to be outside in the midday sun. (8) Even though the desert can be harsh, it can be an interesting place to visit. (9) If you do plan on going to the desert. (10) Wear light-colored clothing and have plenty of water.

© Macmillan/McGraw-Hill

GO ON ➤

Page 6

10 What change, if any, should be made in sentence 3?

   F Change *covers* to **covered**

   G Change *southwestern* to **Southwestern**

   H Insert a comma after *United States*

   J Make no change

11 What change, if any, should be made in sentence 6?

   A Change *completeley* to **completely**

   B Take out the comma after *grown*

   C Change *feet* to **foot**

   D Make no change

12 What change, if any, should be made in sentence 7?

   F Change *it's* to **its**

   G Change *comfortible* to **comfortable**

   H Change *be* to **being**

   J Make no change

13 What change, if any, should be made on sentence 8?

   A Change *can* to **can't**

   B Change *desert* to **Desert**

   C Delete the comma after *harsh*

   D Make no change

14 What is the **BEST** way to combine sentences 9 and 10?

   F If you do plan on going to the desert; wear light-colored clothing and have plenty of water

   G If you do plan on going to the desert, wear light-colored clothing and have plenty of water.

   H If you do plan on going to the desert. Wear light-colored clothing. Have plenty of water.

   J If you do plan on going to the desert, wear light-colored clothing. Plenty of water.

Page 7

BE SURE YOU HAVE RECORDED ALL OF YOUR ANSWERS ON THE ANSWER DOCUMENT.

Student Name _____

Grade 5 • Unit 5 • Week 1
Student Evaluation Chart

Tested Skills	Number Correct	Percent Correct
Reading Comprehension: *Cause and Effect*, 1, 2, 3; *Author's Purpose*, 4	/4	%
Short Answer: *Cause and Effect*, 9	/3	%
Vocabulary Strategies: *Thesaurus: Synonyms*, 5, 6, 7; *Context Clues*, 8	/4	%
Spelling: *Words with Suffixes*, 11, 12	/2	%
Grammar, Mechanics, and Usage: *Appositives*, 10; *Independent and Dependent Clauses*, 13, 14	/3	%

Total Weekly Test Score	**/16**	**%**

Student Name _____

Date _____

Weekly Assessment

TESTED SKILLS AND STRATEGIES

- **Reading Comprehension**
- **Vocabulary Strategies**
- **Spelling**
- **Grammar, Mechanics, and Usage**

McGraw Hill Macmillan/McGraw-Hill

Raymond

1   The sun was just about to slip down below the horizon. Carlton stopped peeling potatoes for a moment. He took in the streaks of orange, pink, and lavender splashed across the sky. For a few seconds, it appeared to him that all movement stopped, both of humans and of animals. Even time appeared to be suspended.

2   Then Hank, the ranch boss, called his name, and everything returned to normal. "You'd better get those potatoes boiling," he said. "They'll be getting back any minute."

3   Hank was referring to the four cowboys who worked on the XIT Ranch. They had been out all day looking after the cattle. The ranch boss had set up camp 60 miles from the ranch house. Carlton was the ranch hand in charge of the cooking at the camp.

4   A short time later, Carlton heard horses' hooves and familiar voices in the distance. In the last light of day, he saw Raymond and the other cowboys approaching. They looked almost tiny in the vastness of the plains. Of the four cowboys, Raymond was Carlton's favorite. He had worked on ranches for over 40 years, and Carlton loved listening to his stories.

© Macmillan/McGraw-Hill

Page 2

5   Carlton sat with the men around a big campfire. They ate the simple meal he had fixed and talked about their work that day.

6   "It took me an hour to rescue a calf from a <u>ravine</u>—probably the deepest one around here," Tom said.

7   The section of the XIT where they were was full of the narrow, rocky valleys. They made the cowboys' work hard and sometimes dangerous.

8   "I'll tell you the toughest part of my day," said Jimmy. "It was when something spooked those three cows and they swerved from the herd. By the time I caught up with them, they'd run a long way in the wrong direction."

9   "But Raymond got to them before you," Pete said, teasing Jimmy.

10   Carlton pictured Raymond beating Jimmy to the three cows. Even though he was well over 60, Raymond rode with a graceful style. And the way he rode, or did anything else at the ranch, showed his enthusiasm. Maybe that was why Carlton admired him so much. Raymond had a passion for his work.

11   As the campfire flickered in the warm breeze, Carlton looked at the older man's face. Over the years, the sun and cold had etched deep creases in it. Raymond never seemed to look worried, but Carlton wondered if he thought about the future. There had been talk of replacing the horses with all-terrain vehicles. Carlton sensed that the continued <u>presence</u> of a man like Raymond on the XIT was none too certain. Someone with fewer skills could easily replace him.

12   Carlton looked down at the campfire and sighed. He had remembered something Raymond had said a few evenings ago: "Nothing in life is certain except change."

Page 3

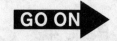

1 Which statement about Raymond is most likely true?

   A He is worried about his future.

   B He does not like working on a ranch.

   C He wants the other cowboys to work harder.

   D He is the best cowboy at the ranch.

2 Where does this story take place?

   F In the forest

   G At a campground

   H In a garden

   J On the plains

3 At the end of the story, how does Carlton feel?

   A Eager to see what the future holds

   B Nervous about what the other cowboys think of him

   C Sad because his days at the ranch are ending

   D Uncertain because life at the ranch may be changing

4 The reader knows that Carlton admires Raymond because Raymond —

   F always catches the cows first

   G tells funny stories

   H is a hard worker

   J taught him how to ride a horse

5 In paragraph 1, what does the word <u>suspended</u> mean?

   A Punished

   B Stopped

   C Improved

   D Supported

6 Which word best completes the analogy? <u>Warm</u> is to <u>cold</u> as <u>vastness</u> is to —

   F largeness

   G smallness

   H emptiness

   J timelessness

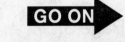

Page 4

7 Which words from the story help the reader understand the meaning of ravine in paragraph 6?

   A *rescue a calf*

   B *Section of the XIT*

   C *narrow, rocky valleys*

   D *toughest part of my day*

8 Which word best completes the analogy? Something is to nothing as presence is to —

   F talent

   G attention

   H weariness

   J absence

9 What does Raymond mean when he says, "Nothing in life is certain except change"? Explain your answer and support it with details from the story.

_____

_____

_____

_____

_____

_____

_____

DIRECTIONS

Read the introduction and the passage that follows. Then read each question and fill in the correct answer on your answer document.

Thanh wrote this story. He wants you to review his work. As you read, think about the corrections and improvements that Thanh should make. Then answer the questions that follow.

Life on a Ranch

(1) It takes many people for a ranch to run smoothly. (2) Ranch bosses, or foremen, are in charge. (3) Working with them are expert horse riders and cattle workers, called cowboys and cowgirls. who work together with ranch hands and helpers. (4) The cowboys and cowgirls are very important, and they have no time to waist. (5) They have to be responsible. (6) may need their help (7) Cowboys and cowgirls start riding horses at a very young age. (8) Their passion for horses and herding cattle is demonstrated in the manor in which they work. (9) Ranch hands take care of the equipment and they feed and care for the animals. (10) Helpers may have a variety of jobs painting fences, cleaning the barns, and gardening. (11) Life on a ranch can be very exciting.

10 What change, if any, should be made in sentence 3?

   F Change *cowboys* to **cowboy**

   G Change the period to a comma

   H Insert a colon after *them*

   J Make no change

11 What is the **BEST** way to combine sentences 5 and 6?

   A They have to be responsible because the animals may need their help.

   B They have to be responsible, the animals may need their help.

   C They have to be responsible because: the animals may need their help.

   D They have to be responsible and, the animals may need their help.

12 What change, if any, should be made in sentence 4?

   F Change *are* to **is**

   G Remove the comma after *important*

   H Change *waist* to **waste**

   J Make no change

13 What change, if any, should be made in sentence 8?

   A Change *Their* to **They're**

   B Change *manor* to **manner**

   C Change *they* to **them**

   D Make no change

14 What change, if any, should be made in sentence 10?

   F Capitalize *gardening*

   G Add a colon after *jobs*

   H Change *variety* to variity

   J Make no change

BE SURE YOU HAVE RECORDED ALL OF YOUR ANSWERS ON THE ANSWER DOCUMENT.

STOP

Student Name _____

Grade 5 • Unit 5 • Week 2
Student Evaluation Chart

Tested Skills	Number Correct	Percent Correct
Reading Comprehension: *Make Inferences, 1, 3, 4; Plot and Setting, 2*	/4	%
Short Answer: *Make Inferences, 9*	/3	%
Vocabulary Strategies: *Context Clues, 5, 7; Analogies: Antonyms, 6, 8*	/4	%
Spelling: *Words with Homophones, 12, 13*	/2	%
Grammar, Mechanics, and Usage: *Independent and Dependent Clauses, 10, 11; Use Colons, 14*	/3	%
Total Weekly Test Score	/16	%

Student Name _____

Date _____

Weekly Assessment

TESTED SKILLS AND STRATEGIES

- **Reading Comprehension**
- **Vocabulary Strategies**
- **Spelling**
- **Grammar, Mechanics, and Usage**

Mc Graw Hill Macmillan/McGraw-Hill

Animal Communities

1   In human communities, people work together. Working together helps us obtain food and shelter, raise children, and enjoy a higher quality of life. When each person contributes to a community, the community functions better. A society needs many different kinds of workers in order to thrive.

2   Animals also live in diverse and varied communities. In fact, nature instills, or implants, most creatures with a social instinct that serves a number of purposes.

3   Many lions work together in well organized groups. The females do the hunting. They work in teams to trap their prey. Because of this, the lions can surround an animal and cut off its escape. Wolves also hunt in teams. They have a strong social order. They follow a leader and obey rules for the good of the pack.

4   Naturalist Dr. Regis Ferriere notes that some insect species exist cooperatively. An example is the relationship between ants and aphids. The ants watch over groups of aphids on grasses as if they were herds of cattle. From time to time, the ants "milk" the aphids of sugar droplets. In turn, the ants protect the aphids from predators.

Page 2

GO ON

5   The members of bee, ant, and wasp communities have special jobs. For instance, a queen and various types of workers live in a beehive. The worker bees serve the queen so the queen can lay eggs. If the queen did not lay enough eggs, the busy hive would soon become vacant. In an ant community, soldier ants protect the colony. In bee and wasp communities, females take on the job of providing protection.

6   Baboons and antelopes often eat together to protect one another. Because the baboons have excellent eyesight and the antelope have a keen sense of smell, together they function as a warning system. Cattle and birds work in much the same way. The birds eat the insects that the cattle stir up. In turn, the birds make a lot of noise and fly off if they sense danger. This warns the cattle. Thus, their combined efforts benefit both the birds and the cattle.

7   Another example of two very different animals helping each other can be found in warm oceans. The remora is a fish that cannot swim well. However, the form of its head allows it to attach itself to large sharks. So it gets from one place to another in the ocean by getting rides from sharks. In turn, the remora cleans the shark of small animals that hurt it.

8   As you can see, there are certain basic similarities between human and animal societies. We have many of the same needs, after all. We must depend on one another to help all survive.

1 In a beehive, worker bees serve the queen in order to —

   A protect the hive from enemies

   B make sure she lays eggs

   C keep wasps from entering the hive

   D collect sugar from the aphids

2 Some ants protect aphids from predators because the ants —

   F want the aphid's sugar droplets

   G are much larger

   H are the leaders of the colony

   J want to do the aphids' work

GO ON ➤

Page 3

3 Look at the chart of information from the article.

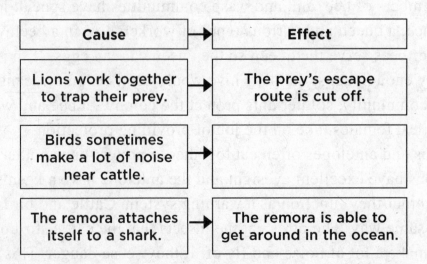

Cause	→	Effect
Lions work together to trap their prey.	→	The prey's escape route is cut off.
Birds sometimes make a lot of noise near cattle.	→	
The remora attaches itself to a shark.	→	The remora is able to get around in the ocean.

Which of these belongs in the empty box?

A The birds clean small animals from the cattle.

B The birds lay eggs.

C The cattle are warned of danger.

D The birds follow their leader.

---

4 When baboons and antelopes eat together, they —

F protect each other

G eat the same food

H develop similar habits

J become natural enemies

5 In paragraph 2, which word from a thesaurus means the opposite of diverse?

A Alike

B Hostile

C Many

D Multiple

Page 4

GO ON ►

6 Which word in paragraph 2 helps the reader understand the meaning of <u>instills</u>?

F *nature*

G *implants*

H *creatures*

J *purposes*

7 Which word means the opposite of <u>vacant</u> in paragraph 5?

A Blank

B Rich

C Occupied

D Abandoned

8 Which word from a thesaurus means the opposite of <u>combined</u> in paragraph 6?

F Mixed

G Joined

H Varied

J Separate

9 Why do people and many kinds of animals live and work together? Explain your answer and support it with details from the article.

_____

_____

_____

_____

_____

_____

GO ON

Page 5

DIRECTIONS

Read the introduction and the passage that follows. Then read each question and fill in the correct answer on your answer document.

Cassie wrote this report for her class. She wants you to review her work. As you read, think about the corrections and improvements that Cassie should make. Then answer the questions that follow.

Dalmatians

(1) Dalmatians are excellent runners and can run for a long time. (2) They are fast than most other kinds of dogs. (3) The Dalmatian is the only breed of dog that seems to smile. (4) A Dalmatian cannot actually smile like people do but it can draw back its lips because of unique muscles in its face. (5) In the United States, Dalmatians are often associated with firehouses. (6) In the past, Dalmatians would run in front of a horse-drawn fire carriage to clear the path. (7) They were sometimes used as rescue dogs in burning buildings. (8) Some people believe Dalmatians are hard to train than other dogs. (9) However, people missjudge this intelligent breed. (10) Dalmatians might sometimes disobey their owners, but they are generally well behaved.

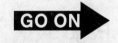

10 What change, if any, should be made in sentence 2?

  F Change *They* to **Them**

  G Change *fast* to **faster**

  H Change *than* to **then**

  J Make no change

11 What revision, if any, is needed in sentence 4?

  A A Dalmatian cannot actually smile like people do: but it can draw back its lips because of unique muscles in its face.

  B A Dalmatian cannot actually smile like people do, but, it can draw back its lips, because of unique muscles in its face.

  C A Dalmatian cannot actually smile like people do, but it can draw back its lips because of unique muscles in its face.

  D No revision is needed.

12 What change, if any, should be made in sentence 8?

  F Change *believe* to **believes**

  G Change *are* to **is**

  H Change *hard* to **harder**

  J Make no change

13 What change, if any, should be made in sentence 9?

  A Take out the comma after *However*

  B Change *missjudge* to **misjudge**

  C Change *this* to **these**

  D Make no change

14 What change, if any, should be made in sentence 10?

  F Change *disobey* to **disobeigh**

  G Change *their* to **there**

  H Change *but* to **so**

  J Make no change

Page 7

BE SURE YOU HAVE RECORDED ALL OF YOUR ANSWERS ON THE ANSWER DOCUMENT.

 STOP

Student Name _____

Grade 5 • Unit 5 • Week 3
Student Evaluation Chart

Tested Skills	Number Correct	Percent Correct
Reading Comprehension: *Cause and Effect,* 1, 2, 3, 4	/4	%
Short Answer: *Cause and Effect,* 9	/3	%
Vocabulary Strategies: *Thesaurus: Antonyms,* 5, 7, 8; *Context Clues,* 6	/4	%
Spelling: *Words with Prefixes,* 13, 14	/2	%
Grammar, Mechanics, and Usage: *Adjectives That Compare,* 10, 12; *Punctuation,* 11	/3	%
Total Weekly Test Score	/16	%

Weekly Assessment

Student Name _____

Date _____

Weekly Assessment

TESTED SKILLS AND STRATEGIES

- **Reading Comprehension**
- **Vocabulary Strategies**
- **Spelling**
- **Grammar, Mechanics, and Usage**

Mc Graw Hill **Macmillan/McGraw-Hill**

Paul Bunyan and Babe the Blue Ox

1   Paul Bunyan is an American legend and a truly original character. The tale of Paul Bunyan has been a part of American folklore for over 100 years. It tells of a brave and giant lumberjack who did giant things.

2   Just how giant was he? Well, three hours after his birth, he weighed 80 pounds. And his fast rate of growth did not stop. After one week he had to wear his father's clothes. The amount of food he ate certainly helped him grow fast. For breakfast, he would eat 40 bowls of oatmeal at once.

3   Paul was enormously brave, too. One of his acts of bravery was to juggle a flaming fireball or two. This would always <u>impress</u> the people watching him. They would applaud with awe and amazement.

4   Paul's special friend was an animal named Babe the Blue Ox. Paul had rescued Babe from drowning, and they had <u>elected</u> to stay together ever since. What a great decision this would be! Babe, who was every bit as big as Paul, began traveling with Paul on his adventures. This unusual pair would find excitement everywhere they would go.

GO ON

Page 2

5   Sometimes, when they had a little free time, the two of them sauntered down to the golf course. Paul did not play golf the way most people do. His golf course was 30 miles wide. The sand trap stretched for acres, like a desert, and the water hazard was a huge lake. Because Paul used cannonballs for golf balls, only Babe was able to carry Paul's enormous golf bag.

6   Babe didn't play the game, but he would watch. Sometimes he would set up a little challenge for Paul. For example, the ox might tell Paul where to hit the ball and see if he could do it. Babe was a polite ox, but he knew how to get Paul riled up. And when Paul was riled up, big things could happen.

7   One day Babe challenged Paul to hit his ball a mile. Paul took a mighty swing, and the ball sailed nine-tenths of a mile—just a tenth of a mile too short. Paul was not at all happy. In fact, he was a little angry. Maybe it was because he had failed the challenge, or maybe it was because of Babe's quiet laugh afterward. Whatever the reason, Paul stomped off without taking his golf tee. You may have seen it just off the highway. A pair of eagles commenced building a nest on top of that tee, and they finished it in about a week.

8   At other times, Paul would lose his golf balls in the huge lake. Babe the Blue Ox became skilled at diving down to retrieve those balls, and then he would wring them dry. That's why Paul gave the huge lake its original name: Ox's Lake. But today you probably know it as Ox Lake in Minnesota.

9   Life for Paul Bunyan and Babe the Blue Ox wasn't just about having fun. When Babe and Paul weren't golfing, they were working at the logging campground. Paul straightened out the curvy logging roads by pulling on the ends of the roads, and Babe opened up the log jams in the river by swishing his tail in the water. People still tell stories about the giant ways Paul and Babe helped the country.

Page 3

1 Look at the chart of information from the story.

Plot	Setting
Paul becomes angry because he fails the challenge.	

Which of these belongs in the empty box?

A An adventure

B The golf course

C The campground

D A huge lake

---

2 How did Paul and Babe meet?

F Paul's father had Babe as a pet.

G Paul saved Babe's life.

H Paul bought Babe at a fair.

J Babe and Paul met on a golf course.

3 Babe helps Paul Bunyan on the golf course by —

A challenging Paul

B giving Paul advice

C finding Paul's golf tees

D carrying Paul's golf bag

4 In paragraph 7, what does the word <u>commenced</u> mean?

F Started

G Challenged

H Finished

J Discussed

5 Which word from the story is a compound word?

A *enormously*

B *oatmeal*

C *rescued*

D *challenge*

GO ON ➡

Page 4

6 In paragraph 3, the word <u>impress</u> means to —

   F have an effect on

   G feel good

   H help in some way

   J ask questions

7 In paragraph 4, what does the word <u>elected</u> mean?

   A Hoped

   B Found

   C Asked

   D Chosen

8 Paul calls the lake Ox's Lake because —

   F Babe hit so many balls into it

   G Paul saved Babe from drowning in it

   H Paul wanted to name it after his friend

   J Babe dove into the lake to get golf balls

9 What is unusual about the golf course that Paul plays on? Explain your answer and support it with details from the story.

_____

_____

_____

_____

_____

GO ON ▶

Page 5

DIRECTIONS

Read the introduction and the passage that follows. Then read each question and fill in the correct answer on your answer document.

Lawrence wrote this paragraph. He wants you to review his work. As you read, think about the corrections and improvements that Lawrence should make. Then answer the questions that follow.

Recycling Drive

(1) The town of Lantana is having a recycling drive on Saturday. (2) Nobody in town feels strongerly about recycling than I do. (3) Boxes, cans, paper, and bottles can be recycled during the drive. (4) We hope this will be the more successful drive ever. (5) Last year, people contributed more than 800 pounds of recyclable materials. (6) This year, the town hopes to pass that goal and collect at least 1,000 pounds! (7) Tom, Luisa, and Rae will work at the recycling drop-off station. (8) They'll start at nine o'clock and work until darknes. (9) Luisa is most experienced than Tom and Rae, but they're all very good workers. (10) We are all hoping that people will realize how effortless it is to recycle and make it a part of their daily lives.

10 What change, if any, should be made in sentence 2?

   F Change *feels* to **feel**

   G Change *strongerly* to **more strongly**

   H Change *do* to **does**

   J Make no change

11 What change, if any, should be made in sentence 4?

   A Change *hope* to **hopes**

   B Change *more* to **most**

   C Change the period to a question mark

   D Make no change

12 What change, if any, should be made in sentence 8?

   F Change *They'll* to **They're**

   G Change *work* to **working**

   H Change *darknes* to **darkness**

   J Make no change

13 What change, if any, should be made in sentence 9?

   A Change *most* to **more**

   B Take out the comma after *Rae*

   C Change *they're* to **he's**

   D Make no change

14 What change, if any, should be made in sentence 10?

   F Change *are* to **is**

   G Change *effortless* to **effortles**

   H Change *lives* to **lifes**

   J Make no change

BE SURE YOU HAVE RECORDED ALL OF YOUR ANSWERS ON THE ANSWER DOCUMENT.

Student Name _____

Student Evaluation Chart

Tested Skills	Number Correct	Percent Correct
Reading Comprehension: *Plot and Setting,* 1, 2, 3, 8	/4	%
Short Answer: *Plot and Setting,* 9	/3	%
Vocabulary Strategies: *Compound Words,* 5; *Context Clues,* 4, 6, 7	/4	%
Spelling: *Words with -less and -ness,* 12, 14	/2	%
Grammar, Mechanics, and Usage: *Using More and Most,* 10, 11, 13	/3	%
Total Weekly Test Score	/16	%

© Macmillan/McGraw-Hill

Student Name _____

Date _____

Weekly Assessment

TESTED SKILLS AND STRATEGIES

- **Reading Comprehension**
- **Vocabulary Strategies**
- **Spelling**
- **Grammar, Mechanics, and Usage**

Mc Graw Hill **Macmillan/McGraw-Hill**

The Nineteenth Amendment

On March 3, 1913, about 8,000 people joined a protest in Washington, D.C.
This march was organized to call greater atention to women's rights.

1   Women in the United States were not always allowed to vote. Instead, women had to fight for the right to vote. They wanted to be able to choose their own representatives and elect the people who shared their ideas. The struggle was difficult and long. It required many people working together to get women the right to vote. These people should be honored for their efforts.

2   In July 1848, a group of women met in Seneca Falls, New York, for the Women's Rights Convention. Susan B. Anthony, Lucy Stone, Lucretia Mott, Elizabeth Cady Stanton, and others joined together to fight for the right to vote. The women had to convince people that they should be allowed to take part in elections. Some people did not think that a woman could qualify to vote.

3   For the next several decades, the women continued their struggle to be able to vote. They made gains in other areas besides voting. In 1870, a woman in Iowa became the first female <u>attorney</u> in the United States. Before that, there had been no women attorneys working in courts of law. In 1872, the U.S. Congress passed a law giving women who worked for the government equal pay for equal work. But in the area of voting rights, there were few gains.

© Macmillan/McGraw-Hill

GO ON

4   Women made speeches and held protest marches all over the country. Bullies tried to break up meetings and events, sometimes with success. However, the women did not <u>submit</u>. They did not even <u>postpone</u> or put off their work. Instead, they kept working courageously for their cause.

5   Finally, the speeches, marches, and meetings began to pay off. In some parts of the country, women were given the right to vote. In 1869, the Wyoming Territory became the first place in the United States to allow women to cast ballots. This was a <u>satisfactory</u> step, but it was only a start. Wyoming was only one territory. But other territories and states soon followed. In 1893, the Colorado legislature gave women the right to vote. Utah and Idaho did so in 1896. Women in the state of Washington were first allowed to take part in elections in 1910.

6   The battle was won in 1919, more than seventy years after it had started. That year, the U.S. Congress passed the Nineteenth Amendment to the Constitution. It stated, "The right of citizens of the United States to vote shall not be denied or abridged by the United States or by any State on account of sex." A majority of the states had to ratify, or approve, the amendment. This was accomplished in 1920, and the Nineteenth Amendment became law. Without the work of these courageous Americans, women might have continued to be denied an important right for an even longer time.

1 In paragraph 3, the word <u>attorney</u> means —

   A leader

   B governor

   C lawyer

   D voter

2 In paragraph 4, what does the word <u>submit</u> mean?

   F Protest

   G Give in

   H Speak up

   J Understand

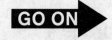

Page 3

3 Which event happened first in the battle for women's voting rights?

A The Colorado legislature gave women the right to vote.

B The Wyoming Territory allowed women to vote.

C The U.S. Congress passed a law giving women who worked for the government equal pay for equal work.

D The U.S. Congress passed the Nineteenth Amendment to the Constitution.

4 Read this dictionary entry.

> pōst • pon´ *v* to put off until a later time [Latin *postpōnere* to put after, lay aside]

The word postpone in paragraph 4 comes from a Latin root that means —

F to give up

G a later time

H to put after

J for women

5 What is the main idea of this article?

A The struggle for women to win the right to vote was long and difficult.

B Susan B. Anthony gave speeches to fight for voting rights.

C Before 1920, only women who worked for the federal government could vote.

D The citizens of some states were reluctant to give women the right to vote.

6 Which word means about the same as satisfactory in paragraph 5?

F Good

G Difficult

H Interesting

J Pleasant

GO ON

Page 4

7 Which sentence from paragraph 6 is an opinion?

    A *The battle was won in 1919, more than seventy years after it had started.*

    B *That year, the U.S. Congress passed the Nineteenth Amendment to the Constitution.*

    C *A majority of the states had to ratify, or approve, the amendment.*

    D *Without the work of these courageous Americans, women might have continued to be denied an important right for an even longer time.*

8 Which sentence from the article is an opinion?

    F *These people should be honored for their efforts.*

    G *Women in the United States were not always allowed to vote.*

    H *In 1870, a woman in Iowa became the first female attorney in the United States.*

    J *Women in the state of Washington were first allowed to take part in elections in 1910.*

9 "Women struggled for many years to win the right to vote." Is this statement a fact or an opinion? Explain your answer and support it with details from the article.

_____

_____

_____

_____

_____

_____

Page 5

GO ON ▶

DIRECTIONS

Read the introduction and the passage that follows. Then read each question and fill in the correct answer on your answer document.

Emilio wrote this report. He wants you to review his work. As you read, think about the corrections and improvements that Emilio should make. Then answer the questions that follow.

New Zoo Opens

(1) The citizens of Bellingham and visitors to our city have something new and exciting to do. (2) They can go to the Lila Benavides Zoo, named for the woman whose generous donation made the zoo possible. (3) The zoo will open next Saturday with some special entertainment that will certainly make a good impresion. (4) Be sure to bring a camera with you to photograph the better collection of animals in the state. (5) This new zoo replaces the old, worn-down zoo which had lesser space for the animals. (6) The cages and enclosures in the old zoo were worst than many zoos around the country, but the new zoo has modern facilities. (7) The zoo's location is easy to find. (8) Come on out and join in the fun!

Page 6

GO ON

© Macmillan/McGraw-Hill

10 What change, if any, should be made in sentence 3?

    F Change *open* to **opening**

    G Insert a comma after *Saturday*

    H Change *impresion* to **impression**

    J Make no change

11 What change, if any, should be made in sentence 4?

    A Change *sure* to **surely**

    B Change *you* to **yours**

    C Change *better* to **best**

    D Make no change

12 What change, if any, should be made in sentence 5?

    F Change *replaces* to **replace**

    G Change *old* to **oldest**

    H Change *lesser* to **less**

    J Make no change

13 What change, if any, should be made in sentence 6?

    A Change *were* to **was**

    B Change *worst* to **worse**

    C Change *has* to **have**

    D Make no change

14 What change, if any, should be made in sentence 7?

    F Change *zoo's* to **zoos**

    G Change *location* to **locasion**

    H Change *easy* to **easiest**

    J Make no change

BE SURE YOU HAVE RECORDED ALL OF YOUR ANSWERS ON THE ANSWER DOCUMENT.

STOP

Student Name _____

Student Evaluation Chart

Tested Skills	Number Correct	Percent Correct
Reading Comprehension: *Sequence, 3; Main Idea and Details, 5; Fact and Opinion, 7, 8*	/4	%
Short Answer: *Fact and Opinion, 9*	/3	%
Vocabulary Strategies: *Context Clues, 1, 2; Dictionary: Word Origins, 4; Synonyms, 6*	/4	%
Spelling: *Words with -ion, 10, 14*	/2	%
Grammar, Mechanics, and Usage: *Comparing with Good and Bad, 11, 13; Irregular Comparative Forms, 12*	/3	%
Total Weekly Test Score	**/16**	**%**

Student Name _____

Date _____

Weekly Assessment

TESTED SKILLS AND STRATEGIES

- **Reading Comprehension**
- **Vocabulary Strategies**
- **Spelling**
- **Grammar, Mechanics, and Usage**

Macmillan/McGraw-Hill

The Big Contest

1   "We'll win this contest," José bragged to Aisha at recess.

2   "How?" Aisha asked. "Why did the fifth grade pick us to represent everyone in the Big Bake-Off? What are we supposed to do? What do we know about baking?"

3   "You don't give us enough credit," José said. "We're capable kids. We know how to follow directions, so using a recipe shouldn't be any problem at all. The contest has many different <u>categories</u> and divisions, and I've got a plan."

4   Suddenly, Aisha's memory went back to a day at recess last year. She saw herself listening to José's big plan. That one had gotten them into big trouble because he made his own rules. They were thrown out of the contest altogether.

5   "Aisha, are you listening to me?" asked José.

6   Aisha shook herself back into the present and asked, "What's your plan?"

7   "We'll bake a gigantic cake. No one will bake a cake larger than ours! Our cake will be so huge that we'll get the prize for the biggest cake," he said.

8   Aisha said, "You know what, José? You're on to something! That's an excellent plan!"

9   The next day, Aisha and José went to the grocery store and bought the ingredients for their cake. At Aisha's house, they set everything on the counter and started working.

10   "We'll bake a few cakes at a time," Aisha said. "Then we'll put them together with a lot of frosting."

GO ON

Page 2

© Macmillan/McGraw-Hill

11   They poured, sifted, stirred, mixed, and baked. While one batch of cakes was in the oven, they started on the next. Much later, Aisha saw the luminous dial on the clock glowing. They had been so busy that they hadn't noticed how dark it had become. Cakes were everywhere, and the kids slumped against the kitchen counter in exhaustion.

12   "My back hurts. I'll never stand up straight again," José moaned as he put all the cakes on a big board.

13   Aisha brushed strands of hair from her eyes. Then she started spreading the frosting. "This part of the cake is soggy," she said.

14   "So it's mushy," José said. "It will dry out by tomorrow. No one will notice."

15   The next day, with the help of Aisha's father and José's mother, the two kids took the huge cake to the school. They left it on one of the special tables set up in the cafeteria for the contest. It was surrounded by many smaller cakes.

16   That day felt like the longest school day ever. Finally it was the last period of the day—time for the contest to begin! All the students at the school went to the cafeteria. They watched as the judges tasted each of the cakes. José and Aisha saw the judges taste the other cakes and smile a lot. But they didn't taste the huge cake.

17   "This looks bad for us," Aisha whispered to José. "What's wrong with our cake? Why won't they even try a bite of it?"

18   "Don't worry, Aisha. We'll win," José said, almost but not quite so sure as he had been the day before.

19   "Look! The judging is over. I'm really nervous," Aisha said.

20   One of the judges cleared his throat and announced, "First prize for the biggest cake goes to . . ." All the students held their breath. " . . . Aisha Thomas and José Mora, representing the fifth grade!"

21   "What did I tell you? It was inevitable that we would win," José said to Aisha with a smile. "I never doubted it for a minute!"

Page 3

GO ON

1 Look at the chart of information about the story.

Character	Plot
Aisha	

Which of these belongs in the empty box?

A Comes up with an idea to make a large cake

B Remembers a past contest where she got in trouble

C Has her parents help her buy ingredients

D Asks the judges why they did not taste her cake

2 How does Aisha probably feel when José first tells her that he has a plan?

F Worried

G Excited

H Confused

J Surprised

3 Which word best describes Aisha?

A Pushy

B Fearful

C Stubborn

D Cooperative

4 An important event takes place in the plot when —

F José tells Aisha they'll win the contest

G José and Aisha shop for ingredients

H Aisha says that part of the cake is mushy

J José and Aisha hear that they have won

GO ON

© Macmillan/McGraw-Hill

5 Which word means about the same as the word <u>categories</u> in paragraph 3?

   A Plans

   B Contests

   C Differences

   D Groups

6 Which word in paragraph 11 helps the reader understand the meaning of <u>luminous</u>?

   F *dial*

   G *clock*

   H *noticed*

   J *glowing*

7 In paragraph 11, the word <u>slumped</u> means —

   A reached

   B sagged

   C pushed

   D cleaned

8 In paragraph 13, the word <u>soggy</u> means about the same as —

   F firm

   G plain

   H wet

   J cooked

9 What kind of person is José? Explain your answer and support it with details from the story.

_____

_____

_____

_____

_____

Page 5

DIRECTIONS

Read the introduction and the passage that follows. Then read each question and fill in the correct answer on your answer document.

Alejandra wrote this story. She wants you to review her work. As you read, think about the corrections and improvements that Alejandra should make. Then answer the questions that follow.

Learning About Space

(1) Today we had an astronot from NASA visit our school. (2) He showed us pictures and a video of the moon. (3) The pictures and video were taken from a satellite that circles the moon very slow. (4) A satellite is like a big computer with a very good camera. (5) I asked him how I could learn more about the moon and the planets. (6) He said I would do goodly by reading books about space. (7) Another way is to read the information and watch the videos on the NASA Web site. (8) He also told us to use a telescope to see the stars, the moon, and the planets. (9) He said if you look very careful, you can see the craters on the moon. (10) I'm going to the library right after school to check out as many books on space exploration as I can!

GO ON ▶

10 What change, if any, should be made in sentence 1?

   F Change *had* to **have**

   G Change *astronot* to **astronaut**

   H Change *our* to **ours**

   J Make no **change**

11 What change, if any, should be made in sentence 3?

   A Change *taken* to **took**

   B Change *circles* to **circling**

   C Change *slow* to **slowly**

   D Make no change

12 What change, if any, should be made in sentence 6?

   F Change *do* to **doing**

   G Change *goodly* to **well**

   H Change *space* to **Space**

   J Make no change

13 What change, if any, should be made in sentence 8?

   A Change *told* to **telled**

   B Change *a* to **an**

   C Change *telescope* to **teleskope**

   D Make no change

14 What change, if any, should be made in sentence 9?

   F Change *look* to **looks**

   G Change *careful* to **carefully**

   H Change *you* to **you'll**

   J Make no change

BE SURE YOU HAVE RECORDED ALL OF YOUR ANSWERS ON THE ANSWER DOCUMENT.

Page 7

Student Name _____

Student Evaluation Chart

Tested Skills	Number Correct	Percent Correct
Reading Comprehension: *Character and Plot*, 1, 2, 3, 4	/4	%
Short Answer: *Character and Plot*, 9	/3	%
Vocabulary Strategies: *Context Clues: Synonyms*, 5, 8; *Context Clues*, 6, 7	/4	%
Spelling: *Words with Greek Roots*, 10, 13	/2	%
Grammar, Mechanics, and Usage: *Adverbs*, 11, 14; *Using* Good *and* Well, 12	/3	%
Total Weekly Test Score	/16	%

Student Name _____

Date _____

Weekly Assessment

TESTED SKILLS AND STRATEGIES

- **Reading Comprehension**
- **Vocabulary Strategies**
- **Spelling**
- **Grammar, Mechanics, and Usage**

Macmillan/McGraw-Hill

A Good Defense

1   One cool Saturday morning, Will slipped out of his house in his favorite jacket with worn, <u>frayed</u> edges and hiked to one of the deep arroyos around Albuquerque. Will had lived in New Mexico his whole life. Yet he never got tired of the beauty of the arroyos. In the summer, the season of sudden storms, these ditches flowed with water. But now, nearly November, the arroyo was <u>parched</u>.

2   Outdoors provided a soothing place to reflect, but Will's thoughts were not calm or happy. He was thinking about the bully who had chased him from the schoolyard on Friday afternoon. And worse, he was thinking about how he had fled like a jackrabbit from the older, stronger boy. His face burned at the unpleasant memory—he didn't want to be a coward.

3   Will sat down at the edge of the arroyo where skunkweed and Apache plume grew freely. The banks of the arroyo offered a secluded home for

the small animals that hid from predators. Snakes, ground squirrels, and rabbits nestled in the soft soil bed of the arroyo. Will gazed at a jackrabbit nibbling the tall grasses. Then he fought down a sinking sensation: a jackrabbit, that's what he was. It was an upsetting thought for Will.

4   Then suddenly, a shadow crossed over him. Will glanced up to see a large hawk wheeling overhead. It hung in the sky for an instant, and Will realized the raptor had gotten a glimpse of the jackrabbit. The jackrabbit froze to avoid arousing its attention. Some animals defended themselves this way, while others turned to fight.

5   The hawk hovered lower in the sky. If that rabbit did not want to be the hawk's meal, it had better move fast. But the little brown fellow seemed stunned by the nearness of the hawk and remained motionless. So the two creatures had recognized one another: hunter and hunted.

6   As the bird swooped lower, Will could hesitate no longer. Abruptly, he grabbed a small stone and flung it right at the jackrabbit. The desperate rabbit leaped away for denser cover in the underbrush.

7   "Good for you," Will thought. "You escaped your foe." Sometimes, he had to acknowledge, it was just wiser to run from trouble.

Page 3

GO ON ▶

1 What problem does Will face in this story?

    A He wants to save a jackrabbit.

    B He cannot go back to school.

    C He needs a way to deal with a bully.

    D He wants to get a new jacket.

2 In paragraph 3, the word <u>sensation</u> means —

    F ability

    G feeling

    H plan

    J cry

3 Which word in paragraph 1 helps the reader understand the meaning of <u>frayed</u>?

    A *slipped*

    B *favorite*

    C *jacket*

    D *worn*

4 Will figures out a solution to his problem by —

    F helping the jackrabbit escape from the hawk

    G watching a hawk hover in the sky

    H listening to the soothing sounds of nature

    J noticing the jackrabbit's stunned reaction

5 In paragraph 6, the word <u>abruptly</u> means —

    A suddenly

    B thoughtfully

    C powerfully

    D angrily

6 In paragraph 1, what does the word <u>parched</u> mean?

    F Overgrown

    G Dry

    H Developed

    J Stable

GO ON

Page 4

7 How does Will help the jackrabbit escape danger?

   A He scares the hawk with a stone.

   B He hides the jackrabbit in the underbrush.

   C He startles the jackrabbit so it runs away.

   D He makes a shadow so the hawk cannot see the jackrabbit.

8 What lesson does this story provide?

   F Once trouble finds you, it is hard to escape.

   G Be careful what you wish for because you just might get it.

   H Sometimes it is wiser to run away than to face danger head on.

   J Ask others for help if you do not know what to do.

9 What similar problem do Will and the jackrabbit face in this story? How do they solve it? Explain your answer and support it with details from the story.

_____

_____

_____

_____

_____

_____

_____

Page 5

GO ON ▶

DIRECTIONS

Read the introduction and the passage that follows. Then read each question and fill in the correct answer on your answer document.

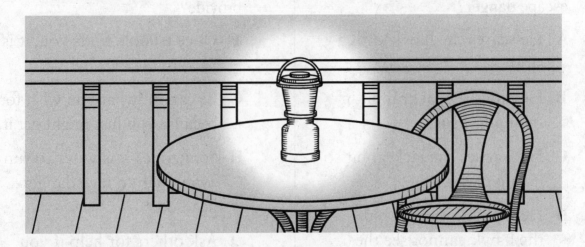

Vanna wrote this note to her friend. She wants you to review her work. As you read, think about the corrections and improvements that Vanna should make. Then answer the questions that follow.

The Stay-Lite Lantern

(1) For my mom's birthday, I got her a beautiful Stay-Lite Lantern to light the backyard. (2) The best thing about this lantern is that it's portible. (3) You can take it anywhere: camping, the beach, or on a hike. (4) It is not very big so you can carry it with you, but it shines brightly than any lantern I have ever seen. (5) The lantern uses energy efficienter than other lanterns and is more durable, too. (6) My little brother dropped it on the ground, but it did not break! (7) I also like that it was made in the United States and not imported from another country. (8) The company delivered the lantern more fast than I expected—it arrived in just two days! (9) I'm glad I got this lantern because my mom loves it.

© Macmillan/McGraw-Hill

GO ON ▶

10 What change, if any, should be made in sentence 2?

   F Change *best* to **goodest**

   G Change *this* to **these**

   H Change *portible* to **portable**

   J Make no change

11 What change, if any, should be made in sentence 4?

   A Change *shines* to **shining**

   B Change *brightly* to **more brightly**

   C Change *seen* to **saw**

   D Make no change

12 What change, if any, should be made in sentence 5?

   F Change *efficienter* to **more efficiently**

   G Change *than* to **then**

   H Change *too* to **two**

   J Make no change

13 What change, if any, should be made in sentence 7?

   A Change *like* to **likes**

   B Change *made* to **maked**

   C Change *imported* to **emported**

   D Make no change

14 What change, if any, should be made in sentence 8?

   F Change *more fast* to **faster**

   G Change *I* to **me**

   H Change the exclamation mark to a question mark

   J Make no change

BE SURE YOU HAVE RECORDED ALL OF YOUR ANSWERS ON THE ANSWER DOCUMENT.

Grade 5 • Unit 6 • Week 2
Student Evaluation Chart

Tested Skills	Number Correct	Percent Correct
Reading Comprehension: *Problem and Solution*, 1, 4, 7, 8	/4	%
Short Answer: *Problem and Solution*, 9	/3	%
Vocabulary Strategies: *Context Clues*, 2, 3, 5, 6	/4	%
Spelling: *Words with Latin Roots*, 10, 13	/2	%
Grammar, Mechanics, and Usage: *Adverbs That Compare*, 11, 14; Using *More* and *Most*, 12	/3	%
Total Weekly Test Score	**/16**	**%**

Student Name _____

Date _____

Weekly Assessment

TESTED SKILLS AND STRATEGIES

- **Reading Comprehension**
- **Vocabulary Strategies**
- **Spelling**
- **Grammar, Mechanics, and Usage**

Mc Graw Hill **Macmillan/McGraw-Hill**

Living Better, Thanks to Inventions!

1   Inventions improve people's lives in many wonderful ways. Most people use marvelous inventions every day and never pause to consider who made them or how great they are. But life would be quite different without the many inventions we have come to rely on.

2   One of the most important inventions was the automobile. This invention forced people to improve roads and turn them from muddy gravel paths into paved highways. It led to the development of suburbs as more and more people moved out of large cities. In addition, the automobile helped people <u>interact</u> with one another by bringing them closer together. People could drive to their jobs or to their friends' and relatives' homes. The distance between places seemed to grow smaller with the arrival of the automobile.

© Macmillan/McGraw-Hill

3   Other inventions help fewer people, but they are no less important. The wheelchair, for example, assists people who cannot walk because of physical problems. A wheelchair is just that—a chair with wheels—although many of them also have motors. All wheelchairs are the same in one way: they all help physically challenged people get around. You may think that this invention will never be of use to you, but you cannot be sure. Anyone could fall and break a leg. A badly broken leg set in an inflexible, rigid plaster cast would keep you off your feet for months. You would be grateful then that the wheelchair had been invented. Nobody should ignore how valuable wheelchairs are.

4   The next time your telephone rings, express your gratitude to Alexander Graham Bell, the man who invented this device. Bell first tested his machine on March 10, 1876, and it quickly became popular. His initial invention opened up a whole new way of communicating. Imagine what life would be like without telephones. The cellular phones so many people have today would never have been invented if it were not for Bell. Most people now think that cellular phones are a necessity of life.

5   Today, much of the work of transmitting phone calls—and thousands of other tasks—is done by computers. Computers are everywhere in the United States, and the country could not function without them. If computers were taken away, traffic would come to a halt. Businesses would close their doors. Lights would go out, and mayhem would ensue. Monica Johns, the successful president of a major company, has called the computer "an indispensable tool in today's economy."

6   Because these inventions are so familiar to us and we use them every day, they may seem simple and elementary. Actually, they are not simple at all, but they have simplified and improved our lives.

Page 3

GO ON

1 The reader can tell that there are glittering generalities in paragraph 1 because the author —

A makes broad and vague statements

B says that everyone agrees with his opinion

C quotes a famous person

D uses words that create strong emotions

2 Which technique of persuasion does the author use in paragraph 3?

F Testimonial

G Comparison

H Causality

J Parallelism

3 The author tries to persuade the reader in paragraph 4 by —

A using a celebrity to promote a product

B claiming that a large number of people think the same way

C using words that appeal to the emotions

D making faulty cause and effect claims

4 How does the author use persuasion in paragraph 5?

F By quoting an expert's opinion

G By giving an unrelated argument

H By making broad statements

J By stating a company's slogan

GO ON

5 Which word means about the same as <u>interact</u> in paragraph 2?

A Relax

B Argue

C Connect

D Play

7 Which word in paragraph 3 helps the reader understand the meaning of <u>rigid</u>?

A *cast*

B *broken*

C *months*

D *inflexible*

6 In paragraph 3, what does the word <u>wheelchair</u> mean?

F A type of furniture

G A vehicle that carries injured people

H A chair with a motor

J A chair mounted on wheels

8 Which word means about the same as <u>elementary</u> in paragraph 6?

F Basic

G Clever

H School

J Troublesome

9 What does the author want readers to think about the importance of inventions? Explain your answer and support it with details from the article.

_____

_____

_____

_____

_____

_____

GO ON

DIRECTIONS

Read the introduction and the passage that follows. Then read each question and fill in the correct answer on your answer document.

Mikayla wrote this story. She wants you to review her work. As you read, think about the corrections and improvements that Mikayla should make. Then answer the questions that follow.

Lucy

(1) Lucy liked to be busy every minute of the day. (2) When she did not have nothing to do, she felt unhappy. (3) Then she would ask everyone in her house, "What can I do for you?" (4) Lucy's mother liked that her daughter offered to help others. (5) But she thought that Lucy should sometimes be still and simply think or sit by the oshean and enjoy the sights, sounds, and smells. (6) One day Lucy's mother said, "Lucy, why don't you go down the street and sit by the beach this morning? (7) Or you can simply sit outside on the terace and watch the birds." (8) "I no have fun relaxing, Mom," Lucy replied. (9) "There are too many more interesting things to do. (10) I do not want to not be still today!"

Page 6

GO ON ➤

10 What is the **BEST** way to rewrite sentence 2?

  F When she did not have nothing to not do, she felt unhappy.

  G When she did not have anything to do, she felt unhappy.

  H When she did have anything not to do, she felt unhappy.

  J When she did not have no anything to do, she felt unhappy.

11 What change, if any, should be made in sentence 5?

  A Change *thought* to **thinked**

  B Change *oshean* to **ocean**

  C Change *enjoy* to **enjoys**

  D Make no change

12 What change, if any, should be made in sentence 7?

  F Change *sit* to **sat**

  G Change *terace* to **terrace**

  H Insert a comma after *and*

  J Make no change

13 What change, if any, should be made in sentence 8?

  A Change *I* to **Me**

  B Change *no* to **don't**

  C Change *relaxing* to **relax**

  D Make no change

14 What is the **BEST** way to rewrite sentence 10?

  F I do not want to be still today!

  G I do want not to be still today!

  H I do want not to not be still today!

  J I do not want to be not still today!

© Macmillan/McGraw-Hill

BE SURE YOU HAVE RECORDED ALL OF YOUR ANSWERS ON THE ANSWER DOCUMENT.

Page 7

Grade 5 • Unit 6 • Week 3
Student Evaluation Chart

Tested Skills	Number Correct	Percent Correct
Reading Comprehension: *Persuasion*, 1, 2, 3, 4	/4	%
Short Answer: *Persuasion*, 9	/3	%
Vocabulary Strategies: *Synonyms,* 5, 8; *Context Clues*, 6, 7	/4	%
Spelling: *Words from Mythology,* 11, 12	/2	%
Grammar, Mechanics, and Usage: *Correct Double Negatives*, 10, 14; *Negatives*, 13	/3	%
Total Weekly Test Score	**/16**	**%**

Student Name _____

Date _____

Weekly Assessment

TESTED SKILLS AND STRATEGIES

- **Reading Comprehension**
- **Vocabulary Strategies**
- **Spelling**
- **Grammar, Mechanics, and Usage**

Mc Graw Hill **Macmillan/McGraw-Hill**

A Matter of Taste

1   Some people claimed that Claudia's grandmother was a superb cook. They even said that she could have been a professional chef in a fancy restaurant. But she preferred cooking for family and friends. Grandma Gillian would set a table with bubbling stews, braided breads, and vegetables simmered in spicy sauces. And her desserts were divine. Whenever she came to visit, Claudia's house began to smell quite interesting.

2   "You should experience foods from other countries, dear," Grandma Gillian informed her. "You would realize that the tastes of people all over the world are <u>reflected</u> in the foods they create. Every civilization has some wonderful foods to offer."

3   But Claudia would eat only a limited number of foods—mainly hot dogs, macaroni and cheese, pizza, and hamburgers. She turned up her nose at her grandmother's dishes with their <u>complex</u> sauces made of many ingredients. She refused to sample those weird foods. Her grandmother never complained about it. She simply threw a hamburger onto the grill. Claudia wondered whether this was part of a <u>strategy</u> to get her to try new foods.

GO ON

Page 2

4   One night Claudia had an unusual experience. The night started out normally enough. Claudia did her homework, ate a hamburger for dinner, read for a while, and went to sleep. But then she dreamed that she floated out of her bed and traveled far away. When she landed, she was in China— at least, that is where she thought she was. A girl took her by the hand and led her to her home, where a feast was in progress. People passed Claudia dishes of hot dumplings, steamed fish, and pork. Everything smelled delicious, and there was no shortage of food. But as she lifted a dumpling toward her lips with chopsticks, she began to float again. She hadn't been able to taste even one morsel of the food.

5   Next, she descended into a desert, where travelers on camels hailed her and invited her to dine with them. A pot of chickpeas and rice simmered in their tent. Each diner got a <u>traditional</u> flat bread with a ladle of stew. The old world recipes stood the test of time. How incredible the food smelled! But once again, Claudia never got even a single bite. Suddenly, she was floating over the earth, her stomach empty. She felt like an outcast.

6   The next day Claudia was exhausted. Her room was bedlam with the pillows tossed off the bed and the blankets all knotted up. Still in her pajamas, she went downstairs to the fragrant-smelling kitchen. She sniffed and asked, "Grandma, what's that wonderful aroma?"

7   The stew pot bubbled merrily, and Grandma Gillian beamed.

---

1 Which new title expresses the author's message in this story?

  A "The Magic Kettle"

  B "The World in a Dish"

  C "Claudia's Nightmare"

  D "Grandma Gillian's Visit"

2 The word <u>complex</u> in paragraph 3 comes from a Latin word that means —

  F coming together

  G strange and unusual

  H unpopular or disliked

  J containing many things

Page 3

3 Look at the chart of information from the story.

| **Detail** |
| Grandma Gillian says that other countries have wonderful foods to offer. |

↓

| **Detail** |
| Claudia dreams that she is not allowed to try foods from other cultures. |

↓

| **Detail** |
| After her dream, Claudia asks her grandmother about the wonderful smell coming from the pot. |

↓

| **Theme** |
| _____ |

Which of these belongs on the blank line?

A Stick to the things you know and like.

B Having a wild imagination can get you into trouble.

C You can learn a lot from experiencing different things.

D It is respectful to be polite to people older than you.

---

4 The word <u>strategy</u> in paragraph 3 comes from a Greek word that means —

F plan

G food

H excuse

J thought

5 In paragraph 5, the word <u>traditional</u> means —

A unique; one of a kind

B made of white flour

C handed down from earlier generations

D shaped like a rounded bowl or pot

GO ON ➡

Page 4

6 Which question best helps identify the theme of the first two paragraphs of the story?

   F How did Grandma Gillian learn to cook?

   G Why do people find different foods tasty?

   H What can be learned from trying new foods?

   J Why do some people cook only for family?

7 In paragraph 2, <u>reflected</u> means —

   A pictured

   B reviewed

   C changed

   D represented

8 Claudia's dream made her feel —

   F cranky because her blankets were on the floor

   G confused because she did not know where she had been

   H unwanted because she felt like she was missing out on something

   J helpless because she did not know how to change her situation

9 What important message about life is expressed in the story, "A Matter of Taste"? Explain your answer and support it with details from the story.

_____

_____

_____

_____

_____

GO ON

Page 5

Read the introduction and the passage that follows. Then read each question and fill in the correct answer on your answer document.

Gerald wrote this story in his journal. He wants you to review his work. As you read, think about the corrections and improvements that Gerald should make. Then answer the questions that follow.

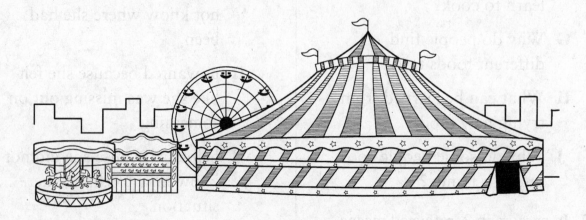

The Circus

(1) My dad took my brother and me for the circus on Saturday. (2) I wasn't sure what to expect, but I had a lot of fun! (3) I liked the elephant show the best. (4) A beautiful lady in a sparkling mask rode on top of the elephant as it lumbered around the ring. (5) I also thought the clown with a goofy uniform was very funny. (6) He acted so silly while he rode his unicycle the circus ring. (7) My dad liked the treo of monkeys that put on a dance show. (8) I think Jake my younger brother mostly enjoyed the food. (9) He ate a hot dog, cotton candy, and an ice cream all in one sitting!

© Macmillan/McGraw-Hill

Page 6

GO ON

10 What change, if any, should be made in sentence 1?

   F Change *me* to **I**

   G Change *for* to **to**

   H Change *on* to **of**

   J Make no change

11 What change, if any, should be made in sentence 5?

   A Change *thought* to **thinks**

   B Change *uniform* to **uneform**

   C Change *was* to **were**

   D Make no change

12 What is the **BEST** way to rewrite sentence 6?

   F He acted so silly while he rode his unicycle around the circus ring.

   G He acted so silly while he rode his unicycle until the circus ring.

   H He acted so silly while he rode his unicycle upon the circus ring.

   J He acted so silly while he rode his unicycle without the circus ring.

13 What change, if any, should be made in sentence 7?

   A Change *My* to **Mine**

   B Change *treo* to **trio**

   C Change *put* to **putted**

   D Make no change

14 What is the **BEST** way to rewrite sentence 8?

   F I think, Jake, my younger brother mostly enjoyed the food.

   G I think Jake, my younger brother mostly enjoyed the food.

   H I think Jake my younger brother, mostly enjoyed the food.

   J I think Jake, my younger brother, mostly enjoyed the food.

BE SURE YOU HAVE RECORDED ALL OF YOUR ANSWERS ON THE ANSWER DOCUMENT.

Grade 5 • Unit 6 • Week 4
Student Evaluation Chart

Tested Skills	Number Correct	Percent Correct
Reading Comprehension: *Theme, 1, 3, 6; Character, 8*	/4	%
Short Answer: *Theme, 9*	/3	%
Vocabulary Strategies: *Context Clues, 5, 7; Word Origins, 2, 4*	/4	%
Spelling: *Words with number prefixes uni-, bi-, tri-, cent-, 11, 13*	/2	%
Grammar, Mechanics, and Usage: *Prepositional Phrases, 10, 12; Commas with Appositives, 14*	/3	%
Total Weekly Test Score	/16	%

Student Name _____

Date _____

Weekly Assessment

TESTED SKILLS AND STRATEGIES

- **Reading Comprehension**
- **Vocabulary Strategies**
- **Spelling**
- **Grammar, Mechanics, and Usage**

Mc Graw Hill **Macmillan/McGraw-Hill**

Whale-Watching

1   Anita's dream had finally come true. She was holding on to the rail of a boat that took tourists to watch whales. The gentle, huge animals had always fascinated her. Then, last fall, her aunt Rachel and cousin Zach had moved to Hawaii. They had invited Anita's family to visit them during Anita's winter break from school. Now they all were on a whale-watching tour boat.

2   A whale <u>emerged</u> from the water by hurling itself up to the surface. With two or three beats of its huge tail, it sailed into the air, and then it fell back into the water with a splash. For a few seconds, it lay sprawled on the ocean's surface. Then its gigantic tail slapped the water a few times. The noise could be heard for a long distance. People watching the attraction from a nearby boat clapped their hands in awe and glee. The whale's showy display had <u>focused</u> everyone's attention on the enormous creature.

3   "Wow!" exclaimed Anita. "That was a humpback, wasn't it, Zach? I never dreamed an ocean animal could reach that size!"

4   Next to her, Anita's cousin Zach nodded. "That one must have weighed 25 tons. But they can weigh even more, you know. Some humpbacks reach 30 tons."

© Macmillan/McGraw-Hill

Page 2

GO ON

5   A collective gasp from the crowd made Anita and Zach turn their attention to the opposite side of the tour boat. The two kids ventured over and were amazed to see another humpback surfacing right next to the vessel.

6   From earlier discussions with Zach, Anita knew that he wanted to be an oceanographer. She just had to inquire, "What do oceanographers do?"

7   "Well," Zach replied, "they do all kinds of things related to the ocean. But I want to study whales in particular. Many species of whales are endangered, mostly because of human activity. I'd like to find ways to save them and increase their populations."

8   Anita looked at the majestic creature. She thought, How odd that it's so close to us—members of the species that have brought it so much trouble. She told Zach, "I think it's a great thing to do. These animals deserve all the help we can give them."

9   Zach nodded as he watched for more whales. "I'm glad you don't think it's unreasonable. It's going to take a lot of people like you and me working for many years to make a difference."

10   The sunshine warmed Anita as she felt the ocean breeze. She looked at the cloudless sky and the dark blue water. She scanned the ocean from left to right and counted six single humpbacks and two pairs. What a wonderful place to work, she thought. At that moment, she made a decision. As soon as she got home, she would do some research on whales and oceanographers. Maybe one day she and Zach would be working side by side.

---

1 In paragraph 2, the word emerged means —

   A discovered

   B appeared

   C floated

   D swam

2 Which word means about the same as focused in paragraph 2?

   F Surprised

   G Pictured

   H Discouraged

   J Concentrated

Page 3

GO ON →

3 Which of these is the best summary of this story?

  A Anita goes to Hawaii to see her cousin Zach, and they go on a boat ride with Aunt Rachel and a group of tourists.

  B While on a whale-watching trip with her cousin Zach, Anita learns that many whales are endangered and decides she wants to learn more about them.

  C Zach knows a lot about whales, likes to share his knowledge with Anita, and hopes to become an oceanographer one day.

  D While on a whale-watching trip, Zach and Anita decide to work together when they get older.

4 What happens just after the crowd of people on the boat gasp?

  F A humpbacks slaps its tail.

  G Zach says that one whale weighs 25 tons.

  H A humpback swims close to the boat.

  J Anita looks at the cloudless sky.

5 The word <u>inquire</u> in paragraph 6 comes from a Latin root that means —

  A ask

  B draw

  C stare

  D move

6 The word <u>unreasonable</u> in paragraph 9 comes from a Latin root that means —

  F swim

  G travel

  H cross

  J think

GO ON ➤

Weekly Assessment

7 Which sentence best summarizes Zach's view of whales?

   A He thinks whales should be protected and helped.

   B He believes whales are the most important ocean animals.

   C He hopes whales will stay away from humans.

   D He thinks people can learn a lot from whales.

8 Which sentence best summarizes what Anita learns from Zach?

   F Humpback whales are found in Hawaii.

   G Humpbacks are the largest whale species.

   H Some whale species are endangered.

   J A whale slaps its tail to communicate.

9 How is the setting of the story important to the plot of "Whale-Watching"? Explain your answer and support it with details from the story.

_____

_____

_____

_____

_____

_____

_____

GO ON

Page 5

DIRECTIONS

Read the introduction and the passage that follows. Then read each question and fill in the correct answer on your answer document.

Julio wrote this story in his journal. He wants you to review his work. As you read, think about the corrections and improvements that Julio should make. Then answer the questions that follow.

Elephants

(1) Mr. Lara works for the Lowry Park Zoo. (2) He told our class about his trip to Africa to study elephants. (3) He said that elephants feel safest when they are together in a group. (4) Then he showed us a photo of a large elephant and two small elephants. (5) He said that the female elephant was the leader except the small elephants were her calves. (6) Mr. Lara also told us that elephants are very smart. (7) He said that some elephants have a special talent, painting! (8) Elephants' trunks are suitible for holding a paintbrush, and their trainers taught them how to do so. (9) I thought this fact was unbelievable, and I would love to see an elephant paint someday.

GO ON

10 What is the **BEST** way to combine sentences 1 and 2?

F Mr. Lara works for the Lowry Park Zoo, he told our class about his trip to Africa to study elephants.

G Mr. Lara works for the Lowry Park Zoo, because he told our class about his trip to Africa to study elephants.

H Mr. Lara works for the Lowry Park Zoo: he told our class about his trip to Africa to study elephants.

J Mr. Lara works for the Lowry Park Zoo, and he told our class about his trip to Africa to study elephants.

11 What change, if any, should be made to sentence 5?

A Insert **but** before *except*

B Change *except* to **and**

C Add **However,** before *He*

D Make no change

12 What change, if any, should be made in sentence 7?

F Change *have* to **has**

G Change *special* to **speshal**

H Change the comma to a colon

J Make no change

13 What change, if any, should be made in sentence 8?

A Remove the apostrophe after *elephants*

B Change *suitible* to **suitable**

C Change *their* to **there**

D Make no change

14 What change, if any, should be made in sentence 9?

F Change *was* to **were**

G Change *unbelievable* to **unbelievible**

H Change *paint* to **painted**

J Make no change

© Macmillan/McGraw-Hill

BE SURE YOU HAVE RECORDED ALL OF YOUR ANSWERS ON THE ANSWER DOCUMENT.

Student Name _____

Grade 5 • Unit 6 • Week 5
Student Evaluation Chart

Tested Skills	Number Correct	Percent Correct
Reading Comprehension: *Summarize,* 3, 7, 8; *Sequence,* 4	/4	%
Short Answer: *Plot and Setting,* 9	/3	%
Vocabulary Strategies: *Context Clues,* 1; *Synonyms,* 2; *Latin Roots,* 5, 6	/4	%
Spelling: *Words with Suffixes -ible, -able,* 13, 14	/2	%
Grammar, Mechanics, and Usage: *Sentence Combining,* 10, 11; *Using Colons,* 12	/3	%
Total Weekly Test Score	**/16**	**%**

Notes

Notes

Notes

Notes